The Art & Science of Emotional Freedom

Your Personal Guide to Positive Change with Meridian Therapies

by

Ananga Sivyer Lic. Tr. AMT MANLP MSAC

First Edition

Second Printing

ISBN 1873483 32 5

Published in the United Kingdom by
DragonRising.com

Published in the United Kingdom by
DragonRising.com
18 Marlow Avenue
Eastbourne
East Sussex BN22 8SJ
United Kingdom

E-mail: books@dragonrising.com
www.DragonRising.com

First Printing March 2000
Second Printing June 2002

Chandra Personal Development Services

Tel: +44 1474 853576
E-mail: chandra@chandra-pds.freeserve.co.uk
Website: www.chandra-pds.freeserve.co.uk

Cover Artwork: G.P. Sivyer

Acknowledgements

Thanks to:
My husband for artwork and moral support.
Gaura for her vision, inspiration and constant encouragement.
Saci for proof reading and feedback.

The following have also offered me support and encouragement for which I am deeply grateful:
Julie and Tracy and all at Mystical Presence, Silvia Hartmann, Jayadeva, Ken, Mum & Dad
and the directors & trainers of The Association for Meridian Therapies

DISCLAIMER

This is a self-help publication and is intended for information and educational purposes only. It is not intended as a substitute for medical or psychiatric attention.

Any reader with a psychiatric or medical condition should first consult with their healthcare practitioner before attempting to use any of the procedures presented within this publication.

If you are in any doubt about the application of these techniques for a major life issue it is strongly recommended that you begin your treatment under the guidance of a licensed practitioner of Meridian Therapies.

Table of Contents

Introduction

Welcome to your personal guide to positive change using the power of meridian therapies. This workbook will introduce you to ground-breaking techniques which you can quickly and easily learn to use for emotional and physical healing.

The primary meridian therapy you will be learning here is The Emotional Freedom Technique™ (or EFT). EFT is a versatile and powerful technique which is accessible to everyone due to its simplicity and convenience of application.

I have always been interested in complimentary therapies and have spent a great deal of time over the years looking into various techniques for reducing stress and anxiety and overcoming personal blockages and limitations. One area that was of particular interest to me (fuelled by my talks with and observations of the courageous battles of people I love dearly) was anything that could ease the pain of abuse or trauma without producing feelings of exposure or vulnerability. A true healing process where the healing and relief could begin immediately without having to go through and go over the very things that were so painful to recall.

I had looked at many techniques by 1999 when I stumbled across the EFT website on the internet. But something here held my interest - the case histories which seemed to meet the above mentioned criteria. I was sceptical at first, I visited the site many times and read and re-read the information. Eager to find out more I made contact with Silvia Hartmann-Kent, the UK contact I found listed on the site, her conviction and enthusiasm prompted me to try out EFT for myself. And the rest is history! Albeit it recent history. EFT has changed my life and the lives of several people around me very much for the better.

The aim of this workbook is to present these valuable and highly effective techniques in a way that can be easily learned by anyone who wishes to try the power of meridian therapies for themselves.

The first part of this book (the "science") provides a basic understanding of the meridian system and covers the history and development of the techniques presented.

After the science you will find the "art" - for those of you who want to get straight to the business of setting down your emotional baggage and walking away from it. This is where you can begin learning the tools that you will use for a lifetime.

Should you wish to explore these techniques further via workshops or professional training please refer to the contact information at the back of this book.

With my best wishes
Ananga Sivyer

"EFT is a Doorway to the new Healing High-Rise. It is the place where a growing number of newcomers to this exciting field get their start. We now have thousands of practitioners using EFT throughout the world.

I hope this doesn't sound too grandiose, but I've been doing energy healing work since 1991 and my jaw still drops at the results. I've lost count of the number of phobias, traumatic memories, guilt, grief and physical ailments that have been elegantly relieved (often in minutes) by this procedure. Even though EFT violates just about every conventional belief out there, the results remain remarkable. EFT isn't perfect, of course. We don't get 100%. But it usually works well and the results are sometimes spectacular."
Gary Craig
Developer—Emotional Freedom Techniques

CHAPTER 1

Overview & History

An Overview of the Meridian System

The techniques we have come to know today as "energy" or "meridian" healing originated in Ayurveda, the oldest and most comprehensive medical science. The major and minor chakras and their interconnecting networks, pressure points and breathing techniques are all thoroughly documented in ancient Indian texts dating back over 5,000 years.

Ayurveda provides detailed information on vital sensitive points located on the skin surface. Specific massage techniques are used to stimulate and balance these *marmas* as they are called in the original texts. These potent points are mapped out precisely with detailed information on function and location.

Chinese acupuncture and it's understanding of the Meridians is believed to be a direct descendant of this system. The Asian martial arts traditions and the principles of Ayurveda show remarkable similarities, including use of specific vital points.

This medical knowledge travelled to China with Buddhist missionaries in the early centuries. It is from this source that Traditional Chinese Medicine draws its wealth of knowledge on the integration of psychology, physiology, environment and constitution for therapeutic attention.

More recently, direct links have been drawn between the works of the surgeon Sushruta who lived some 2,000 years ago and the highly developed systems of pressure points and meridians still in use to this day.

Recent breakthroughs and developments in the field of Meridian Therapies have provided healthcare practitioners the world over with a new collection of groundbreaking techniques for providing quick and often permanent relief from negative emotional states.

These techniques are based upon ancient healing sciences dating back over five thousand years which present an understanding of the energy, or meridian, system of the body.

The Meridians are also referred to as channels, vessels, or pathways. These channels form a continuous network throughout the body; running up and down the trunk, head and limbs and throughout the internal organs, transporting the vital energy known as *Chi* in oriental medicine, or *prana* in Ayurvedic medicine.

There are 14 main meridians in the human body. Of these 12 are associated with one of the principle internal organs and is named according to that association. There are twelve paired or bi-lateral Meridians found symmetrically in the body namely: the lung, large intestine, stomach, spleen/pancreas, heart, small intestine, bladder, kidney, pericardium, triple burner, gall bladder and liver. The additional 2 Meridians are also referred to as vessels and are called the Conception and Governing Vessels.

Energy flows from one end to the other through these channels, which lie just below the surface of the skin. The end of each meridian has a deep channel where it connects to the beginning of the next one thus forming a continuous cycle.

The energy flowing through this system also radiates beyond the surface of the skin in a similar way to a magnetic field.

The Meridians of the body can be stimulated and assisted in promoting unhindered flow by various natural methods such as: massage, finger pressure, or percussion (tapping on) key meridian points.

The basis of acupuncture theory is that by working with points on the surface of the body the internal functioning of the body can be affected and balanced by manipulating the Chi energy. These surface points are key points situated along the different meridians, which respond to stimulation or sedation as required.

When the energy flow, or circulation of chi, is unrestricted in it's journey through the Meridian system both body and mind exhibit harmony and balance. However, lifestyle, abuses, stress etc. upset that balance. If such abuses and stresses go unchecked and are allowed to accumulate then disturbance and health problems will soon manifest.

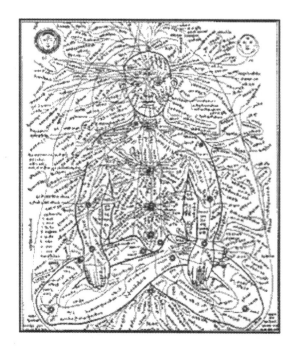

Diagram showing the interconnection between the chakra's and subtle energy channels

There is a direct relationship between the quality of a person's emotions and their physical health. Each meridian/internal organ is directly connected with a specific range of emotions. Organs exert influence on the expression of particular emotions and the organ function is, in turn, affected by those emotions. Thus forming a two-way cycle of influence.

Therefore, little distinction is made between the body and the mind in diagnosis. With this in mind, we can clearly see how the emotions play their role in the cause of disease.

The classical texts of Chinese acupuncture present a total of 59 Meridians, as listed below:

The 12 main Meridians and their branches

The eight extra Meridians

The 12 divergent Meridians

The 12 muscle Meridians

The 15 connecting Meridians

In general practice, only 14 of the above the Meridians are used. They are the 12 main Meridians and two of the eight extra Meridians, namely, the conception and governing vessels. The 12 main meridians are each associated with one of the principle internal organs and are, therefore, named according to that association. These twelve Meridians are paired, or bilateral, and are situated symmetrically on either side of the body.

They are: *the lung, large intestine, stomach, spleen, heart, small intestine, bladder, kidney, pericardium (or circulation/sex), triple warmer, gall bladder and liver.* The two extra meridians are the conception and governing vessels.

The vital life force, or Chi, flows constantly throughout the 12 meridians of the body starting with the lungs, following then through the large intestine, stomach, spleen, heart, small intestine, bladder, kidney, pericardium, triple warmer, gall bladder, and ending in the liver. Without this energy constantly circulating there would be immediate death.

This cycle flows in the following order throughout the body:
from the torso to the fingertip (along the inside of the arm)
from the fingertip to the face (along the outside, or back, of the arm)
from the face to the feet (down the outside of the leg)

This pattern is repeated three times to form a cycle throughout the twelve major meridians.

Although the energy flow through the meridians is a continuous cycle, each channel contains it's own unique type of energy according to it's associated organ.

Whilst fundamentally the same type of energy, the chi energy related to each of the individual organs differs in nature in order to exert different influences upon those organs. For example: the energy flowing through the heart meridian controls the functions of the heart both physiologically and psychologically, the energy flowing through the large intestine meridian does the same for it's associated organ which, obviously, has a very different set of functions from the heart.

Meridians are also classified as *yin* or *yang* according to the direction in which they flow on the surface of the body. When standing with the arms above the head, all Yin meridians flow upwards, while Yang meridians flow downwards.

Each meridian is paired with a yin or yang counterpart as indicated in the table below:

YIN	YANG
Lung	Large Intestine
Heart	Small Intestine
Pericardium	Triple Warmer
Spleen	Stomach
Liver	Gall Bladder
Kidney	Bladder

Each meridian possesses a particular characteristic or quality, which exerts its influence on the body and mind. The nature of these influences depends upon the condition of the particular meridian i.e. whether it is balanced, under or overactive. In general, balanced flow ensures balanced health and emotional responses.

CHAPTER 2

The Meridians

Meridians & The Major Organs

"In Traditional Chinese Medicine the Organs are seen not just as physical body parts, but in terms of their functions and relationships with other parts of the body. There is some overlap with the Western physiological definition, but in general the Chinese definition of an Organ encompasses the related spiritual and emotional systems, as well as the physical."
Maria Mercati - Step by Step Tui Na

The Chinese Medical understanding teaches that although the level of chi energy present in the body is a key factor in overall health, it's distribution, quality and balance throughout the meridian system is of equal importance. The meridian system is responsible for the distribution of chi throughout it's intricate network thus nourishing and influencing body, mind and spirit.

We don't need to be concerned with diagnostic methods to use the techniques presented here, the information on meridian qualities that you will find on the following pages is intended only as a brief but useful insight to the mind/meridian connection. To study the meridians in depth requires a great deal more information (please see the recommended reading list for details of some publications which cover the meridians in greater depth).

The Lung Meridian

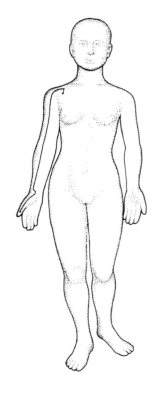

Table of Properties:

Meridian Flow:	Toward the thumb from the inside edge of the front of the shoulder.
Most active time:	3.00-5.00 AM
Associated Element:	Metal
Companion Organ:	Large Intestine

LUNG FUNCTION

The function of the lungs is to directly control the process of respiration, and to indirectly influence the heart and circulatory system.

Pure chi is drawn from the air by the lungs on inhalation. And via exhalation they return "impure" or "dirty" chi. In this way, the process of respiration is fundamental to the renewal and purity of bodily chi. The lungs also regulate chi in the chest area in general sent up from the spleen from the processing of nutrients.

According to Traditional Chinese medicine, the lungs house the corporeal soul, which is, by nature, optimistic and open to new experiences and opportunity. Reduced vitality and constricted breathing are the negative results of constriction to the lungs and corporeal soul.

GENERAL CHARACTERISTICS:

Each organ team of the meridian system has an associated bodily sense as one of its offspring; in the case of the lung/large intestine team it is the sense of smell.

Each team also has its own way of releasing stress and tension as a protective measure against accumulation and the development of disease. The lung/colon team use the following methods of expression as their "release valve": weeping, lamenting, sobbing or wailing etc.

Healthy balance of the lung meridian is indicated by good animal drive, a well-developed survival instinct, will power, quick perception, willingness and ability to fight for beliefs if necessary, as well as by the obvious physiological indication of good respiration.

Breathing is an essential factor in our general well being, each breath influences our emotional perception to a degree; inhaling is uplifting and stimulating; exhaling is relaxing and sedating.

If the lung meridian is imbalanced strong emotions are sure to manifest. The lung/colon team is associated with the metal element and the primary negative expression of metal is grief.

Worry, anxiety, sorrow, melancholy and resentment are other negative emotions associated with the lungs and are considered extreme manifestations of the qualities exhibited when the lung meridian is balanced.

Some symptoms of general imbalance:
Chest congestion, coughing, pain or discomfort upon deep inhalation or exhalation, anguish, sinus problems, holding of the breath, nasal congestion, hoarseness.

Associated Physiological Areas:
The skin, nasal passages, thumb (note the path of this meridian), body hair, mucus membranes, respiration in general.

Psychological Qualities of Balance:
Compassion, good survival instinct, instinct and intuition, free will, individuality, positive outlook, endurance.

Psychological Qualities of Imbalance:
Sorrow, resentment, worry, coughing, anguish, claustrophobia, inflexibility (both body and mind), pessimism, nostalgia.

The Large Intestine Meridian

Table of Properties:

Meridian Flow:	Beginning either side of the nostrils running across the shoulder and down the arm to the index finger
Most active time:	5.00-7.00 AM
Associated Element:	Metal
Companion Organ:	Lung

LARGE INTESTINE FUNCTION

The large intestine receives food and fluids from the small intestine, it absorbs fluids and nutrients and eliminates the remaining unwanted matter as waste.

Regular elimination of waste is essential in the avoidance of toxic build up and is essential in maintaining good health.

The lungs have influence over the large intestine as they are responsible for descending chi energy—if the large intestine does not receive enough chi to encourage the elimination of waste constipation will often result. According to the theory of Chinese Medicine this explains the common occurrence of constipation in the elderly - as lung chi is often found to be deficient in elderly people.

Together, the large intestine and lung team are concerned with elimination in general—the lung eliminates carbon dioxide, the waste product of respiration; and the large intestine eliminates solid waste matter. In psychological terms due to their relationship with the metal element the lung/large intestine team are responsible for "letting go" which can be seen as the mental equivalent of the physical elimination processes.

Traditional understanding clearly indicates that there is a mental as well as physical "constipation" manifesting as the inability to eliminate unnecessary and unwanted thoughts, resulting in the accumulation of toxic feelings and ideas and the long-term contamination of the mind. For individuals afflicted with an imbalance of this nature prolonged and constant preoccupation with injustices and "ills" whether perceived or factual is extremely likely.

GENERAL CHARACTERISTICS:

Like it's partner, the lungs, the large intestine will often reveal imbalances via the skin, excessive mucus and discharge from the eyes or nose.

Poor posture, stooping in one position through work for long periods or laying down for excessive periods is detrimental to the lung energy.

Some symptoms of general imbalance:

Constipation, lack of body heat and dry lips are considered indications of under activity in the large intestine. Over activity may be indicated by: dizziness, stiffness in the shoulders or arms, headaches, nose bleeds, a tendency to overeat.

Psychological Qualities of Balance:

Compassion, good survival instinct, instinct and intuition, free will, individuality, positive outlook, endurance. As per the lung and metal element.

Psychological Qualities of Imbalance:

Sorrow, resentment, worry, coughing, anguish, claustrophobia, inflexibility (both body and mind), pessimism, nostalgia. Stubbornness, holding on.

The Stomach Meridian

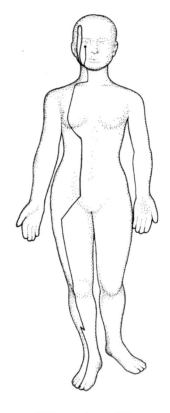

Table of Properties:

Meridian Flow:	From under the eye up and around the side of the face - then down the torso ending in the second toe.
Most active time:	7.00-9.00AM
Associated Element:	Earth
Companion Organ:	Spleen (and pancreas)

STOMACH FUNCTION

The stomach is considered a particularly important organ in Chinese Medicine. It's primary function is to prepare the food we eat for refinement by the spleen and sorting by the small intestines. The stomach is the primary focus of bodily nourishment.

Along with it's partner organ, the spleen, the stomach is responsible for the delivery of nutrients derived from food to the entire body, especially the muscles and limbs. It is common for a person to tire easily and experience heaviness of their limbs if the stomach is weak.

GENERAL CHARACTERISTICS:

The self, or ego, is usually placed under the care of the spleen/stomach team; consequently, emotional attachments such as addictions, clinginess, rigid thinking, persistence and excessive self-interest are usually attributed to these organs.

Just as the stomach is the centre for bodily nourishment it is similarly concerned with nourishment of the mind specifically through the digestion and assimilation of ideas. The stomach energy is responsible for breaking down information for assimilation and mental processing. An "empty feeling" born of imbalance in the stomach meridian will often result in a cravings for food on the physical level and stimulation mentally or emotionally. An interesting insight to the common phenomena of eating when "bored" or never feeling satisfied or "full".

Imbalances within or between this organ team are also found in other ways such as:

anxiety (in combination with the lungs/colon), forgetfulness (in combination with the liver/gall bladder team and other organs), mouth problems and craving for or reaction to sweets.

A balanced and healthy stomach will express itself by humming, singing, positive ideas and creativity.

Some symptoms of general imbalance:
Dry tongue, stuffy nose, abdominal distension after eating, feelings of suspicion or mistrust

Psychological Qualities of Balance:
Stable "centred" emotions, confidence, good taste, an understanding of appropriate behaviour, a sense of trust, considered thought and action.

Psychological Qualities of Imbalance:
Anxiety, worry, scepticism, poor confidence.

The Spleen Meridian

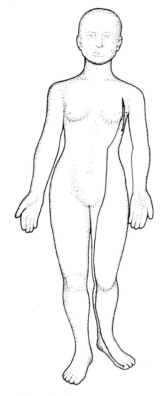

Table of Properties:

Meridian Flow:	From the big toe, up the inside of the leg, toward the shoulder and down to finish on the side under the arm
Most active time:	9.00-11.00AM
Associated Element:	Earth
Companion Organ:	Stomach

SPLEEN FUNCTION

The primary function of the spleen meridian (which includes the pancreas as part of it's functional unit) is the processing of food and fluids into energy for the nourishment (food chi), it is then responsible for the delivery of nutrients throughout the body.

The spleen energy is also responsible for raising chi in a general sense - via it's "lifting" influence it holds the internal organs in place; imbalances in this function result in prolapse or hernias.

GENERAL CHARACTERISTICS:

A healthy spleen ensures good digestion and absorption and a healthy appetite. The spleen is also responsible for stabilizing the circulation of blood. The health of the lymphatic organs is dependant upon the balance of the spleen and pancreas.

The spleen houses "thought" and is concerned with analysing, concentration and study as well as thinking in general. In balance the spleen meridian will exhibit the qualities of memory, concentration and a clear and constructive thought process. Conversely, a deficiency in spleen chi will manifest in unclear thought and poor concentration. In such cases of imbalance much effort and mental energy is spent in reaching conclusions - this "over thinking" further depletes spleen energy thus establishing a vicious cycle.

These organs are injured by excess exercise or physical labour, over eating and sitting for prolonged periods. The spleen is considered the home of stubbornness and persistence; an individual's sense of loyalty and rigidity - both mentally and physically are greatly influenced by this organ team (these traits also manifest as a characteristic of the lung/colon team).

22

Some symptoms of general imbalance:

Insomnia, abdominal bloating, PMT and menstrual problems, swelling of legs and ankles, obesity, low energy, obsession, stuffy nose, heavy limbs, poor digestion, ulcers.

Psychological Qualities of Balance:

Reasoning abilities, memory, a clear thought process, honest introspection, opinion, loyalty, willpower, sense of satisfaction/achievement, ideas & creativity, sympathy.

Psychological Qualities of Imbalance:

Worry, poor concentration, forgetfulness, cloudy thought process, vacillation, addiction, attachment, obsession, gluttony, jealousy, self-pity, strong concern about opinions of others, stubbornness, vanity.

The Heart Meridian

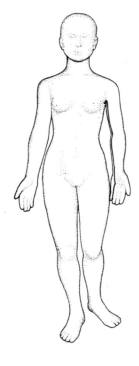

Table of Properties:

Meridian Flow:	From under the armpit down the arm to the back of the little finger (towards the ring finger).
Most active time:	11.00AM - 1PM
Associated Element:	Fire
Companion Organ:	Small Intestine

HEART FUNCTION

Of the four organs/meridians that come under the control of the fire element, the heart is considered the most important. It has two primary functions - to govern the blood and blood vessels and to house the mind. The heart and it's partner, the small intestine, are likened to the motor and fuel tank of a vehicle. They are the home of the vital energy and the spirit.

The Western Medical understanding of the heart as a pump is also accepted in Traditional Chinese Medicine. However, Oriental Medicine also views the heart as the final stage in the production of the blood; the heart being the site where chi energy derived from food is transformed into blood.

GENERAL CHARACTERISTICS:

The heart controls the blood vessels and is responsible for the quality of the pulse. It also manifests the complexion thus demonstrating the link between good circulation and a healthy complexion.

Speech is governed by the heart; speech impediments and stuttering are connected to imbalances of this organ/meridian. Laughing without apparent reason and incessant talking are considered to be manifestations of imbalanced heart energy.

The primary emotions of the heart are joy (in balance) or sorrow. Not surprisingly, the heart is considered the "king" or centre of our emotional existence. Due to it's core position in our emotional well being the heart is easily affected by any extreme emotion in conjunction with the organ team specifically related to the specific emotion being expressed. For example, grief would affect the heart in conjunction with the lungs and their partner the large intestine as the organs directly connected to that specific emotion.

Some symptoms of general imbalance:

Hot flashes, stuttering, inappropriate laughter, over-excitement, insomnia, hysteria, frequent thirst, angina, general stiffness, shoulder pains, sensitivity to touch, night sweating, discomfort in lying down.

Psychological Qualities of Balance:

Tranquillity, gentleness, emotional balance, spirit, love, integrity, optimism, emotional and spiritual growth, zest for life, control of thoughts and senses, conscience, wisdom.

Psychological Qualities of Imbalance:
The heart is the ruler of all emotions. Hysteria, erratic behaviour, alternating joy and melancholy, dullness, yearning for love, jealousy, sorrow.

The heart is imbalanced by excessive heat of any kind (drinks, weather, clothing etc.) fright or terror, extreme emotions of any sort, dark thoughts.

The Small Intestine Meridian

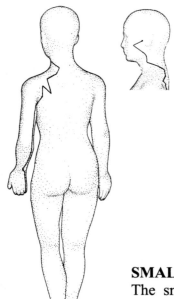

Table of Properties:

Meridian Flow:	From the end of the little finger up the outside of the arm, over the shoulder ending in front of the ear.
Most active time:	1.00-3.00PM
Associated Element:	Fire
Companion Organ:	Heart

SMALL INTESTINE FUNCTION

The small intestine continues the digestive process by receiving partially digested matter from the stomach and separating nutrients from waste. This is also considered the beginning stage in the formation of the blood.

The small intestines discriminatory role in sorting matter during digestion extends to the mental realm where it is strongly influential in decision making and clarity of thought.

The small intestine is the partner of the heart and serves to protect it by taking on the main bulk of any abuses before they affect the heart directly; many of the heart symptoms of disturbance also belong to the small intestine. One of the key areas in which the small intestine protects the heart is by the elimination of heat which, as described in the heart meridian information, is greatly detrimental to the heart in excess.

Some symptoms of general imbalance:

Anaemia (begins in the small intestine), bloody stools or urine, pain in the temple, restlessness, overworking, rapid eating, keeping feelings held inside, neck pain, difficulty in turning the head, frequent bowel movements, poor circulation in extremities, malfunction of ovaries.

Psychological Qualities of Balance:

Memory, ability in making decisions, clarity of thought

Psychological Qualities of Imbalance:
Forgetfulness, indecision, unclear thought process

The negative emotion which is most injurious to the small intestine is envy or jealousy, which leads to heart and digestive problems.

The Bladder Meridian

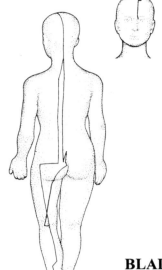

Table of Properties:

Meridian Flow:	Begins at the corner of the eye, continues over head, down back and legs, ending on small toe.
Most active time:	3.00-5.00PM
Associated Element:	Water
Companion Organ:	Kidney

BLADDER FUNCTION

The urinary bladder is the partner of the kidneys - this team is responsible for the regulation of the body's water and is directly under the control of the water element. Physically the urinary bladder is concerned with the storage and release of excess fluids (as urine).

GENERAL CHARACTERISTICS:

As the partner of the kidneys, the psycho-emotional function associated with the bladder is restraint. In balance the bladder manifests the qualities of healthy caution and good judgement; however, if abuses are allowed to accumulate these qualities become distorted and the bladder will manifest fear, nervousness and a lack of confidence.

Determination, will power and ambition will be lacking when the kidney/bladder team is out of balance.

The energy related to memory is under the control of the bladder organ/meridian. It is viewed as a reservoir of energy which includes mental energy. Imbalance here would manifest in lack of ability to cope and fear of being submerged or overwhelmed.

The outer line of the bladder meridian house the "Shu" points - or associated points - these points are of particular importance in acupressure and acupuncture treatments as they directly connect to other organs and meridians. For this reason, the bladder meridian is strongly indicated in Chinese medicine in the treatment of emotional imbalance and disorder.

"Each point outside of an "Associated Effect Point" makes a direct connection with a Zang (Yin) Organ and has a particular emotional, mental, or spiritual significance."
Leon Hammer M.D. - Dragon Rises, Red Bird Flies

The first treatment point in the EFT sequence (as will be shown later) is situated on the bladder meridian.

27

Some symptoms of general imbalance:

Trembling, stress, restlessness, tension in shoulders, worry over small details, pain in spine, pain around waist, inflammation or pain in bladder, frequent urination, poor circulation.

Psychological Qualities of Balance:

Caution, restraint, determination, will power, ambition.

Psychological Qualities of Imbalance:

Fear, lack of confidence, nervousness, fear of being submerged or overwhelmed, strained nerves, hypersensitivity (physical and emotional).

The bladder is severely affected by the retention of urine.

The Kidney Meridian

Table of Properties:

Meridian Flow:	Begins in the centre of the sole of the foot, travels up inside leg to collar bone.
Most active time:	5.00-7.00PM
Associated Element:	Water
Companion Organ:	Bladder

KIDNEY FUNCTION

The primary function of the kidneys is the storage of the vital essence—this essence governs the processes of birth, growth, reproduction and development. Therefore, the kidneys are concerned with individual development according to each person's unique plan or inherited code (see inherited chi in notes).

The job of the kidney essence is to maintain this plan against external influences (such as climate, environment etc.) Mental and physical growth and development manifest over time under the influence of the Kidney essence (or jing). Imbalance or afflictions here may be manifest in stunted growth or premature ageing.

GENERAL CHARACTERISTICS:

Poor kidney function is readily revealed by a dark or blackish colour in the complexion, in particular darkness beneath the eyes.

The primary emotion attributed to the kidneys is fear. In balance this is reflected in caution and good judgement; however, imbalance will manifest in fearfulness, retreat and nervous distress.

The kidneys are closely related to the lungs and receive the chi sent down by the lungs on inhalation.

The kidneys are responsible for the development of head hair, the bones and skeletal structure and the water content of the blood. They are also directly connected to sexual drive and the production of reproductive and developmental hormones.

Some symptoms of general imbalance:

Bladder weakness, sexual problems, infertility, varicose veins, weakness of the ankles, kidney stones, skin problems, nail biting, hair loss, painful joints, imbalanced hormone secretion, poor sleep habits.

Psychological Qualities of Balance:

Restraint, humility, spiritual surrender, organisational skills, will power, ability to concentrate, good imagination, ideas, self-preservation, "zest" for living, ability to control the mind and avoid unwise action, determination, respect and reverence, courage, confidence, sense of security.

Psychological Qualities of Imbalance:

Fear, hesitancy, no "zest" for life, poor willpower, sexual frustration, guilt, nervousness, lack of confidence, depression, trembling, would rather run from situations than deal with them.

The kidneys are severely affected by salt (to much or too little), meat, harsh sugars, excessive standing, kneeling or sexual activity, sitting on damp ground and lifting.

The Pericardium Meridian

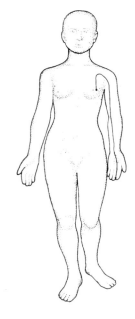

Table of Properties:

Meridian Flow:	From the chest down the arm to the middle finger.
Most active time:	7.00-9.00PM
Associated Element:	Fire
Companion Organ:	Triple Warmer

PERICARDIUM FUNCTION

The pericardium meridian is sometimes referred to by two other names each describing it's major functions: the "circulation-sex" meridian - due to it's encompassing the entire cardio-vascular system and it's close relation to sexual drive; and the "heart protector".

In it's role as heart protector the pericardium physically protects the heart from shock and stress by surrounding it with a protective fibrous sac. The pericardium assists the heart in it's functions of governing the blood and housing the mind and is directly responsible for the circulation of the blood and the pulse rate. It's psychological responsibility is to control the emotions; in this way the pericardium endeavours to protect the heart from the damaging effects of serious emotional imbalances.

The heart and pericardium have a great influence over our expressive abilities and relationships in general. The pericardium reflects the way we express ourselves externally and our relationships with others. The degree of our ability to express warmth and concern for others falls directly under the control of this meridian; whereas the heart gives an indication of our internal expression - the way we relate to ourselves.

When speaking of energy or the life force circulating around the body-mind system the speed or intensity of that energy is more relevant than amount. For example, if somebody states that they have too little energy the reality is more likely to be an inhibited or erratic flow of energy rather than there actually being "too little" present. Conversely, energy moving too quickly from organ to organ would result in a feeling of "too much energy" which might manifest in boredom or a desire to "do something" to spend energy. Such expressions give a good indication of the pericardium's condition in it's role as governor of the circulatory process.

Some symptoms of general imbalance:

Shallow and or dream-filled sleep, swollen armpits, promiscuity, hysteria, hysterical or cackling laughter, palpitations, shortness of breath, abnormal emotional responses, hyper-sensitivity, poor sleep habits, easily fatigued.

Psychological Qualities of Balance:

Love, happiness, contentment, warmth and concern in relationships, enthusiasm.

Psychological Qualities of Imbalance:

Sadness, sorrow, grief, self– absorption, coldness, lack of concern, poor relations with others, lack of enthusiasm.

The Triple Warmer Meridian

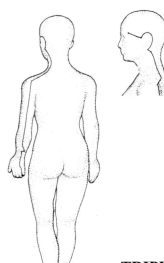

Table of Properties:

Meridian Flow:	From the ring finger up the back of the arm, over the shoulder ending above and to the outside of the eye.
Most active time:	9.00-11.00PM
Associated Element:	Fire
Companion Organ:	Pericardium

TRIPLE WARMER FUNCTION

The triple warmer is the odd one out of the meridian system because it is not an "organ" of the body, rather it is the combination of other teams producing a specific glandular function.

This meridian is also referred to as the triple heater or burner, as these names imply, it's primary function is to create or sustain warmth; the upper warmer occupies and warms the area above the diaphragm, the middle heater regulates the area between the diaphragm and the naval and the lower heater is responsible for the area below the naval.

The Yellow Emperor's Classic (*Nei Jing*) describes the triple warmer meridian as " the official in charge of irrigation and the control of water passages." In fulfilling this function, each of the three regions produces and controls a different type of body fluid - the upper warmer produces a mist and distributes fluids throughout the body as a vapour; the middle warmer is described as a bubbling cauldron, the place of digestion and the distribution of nutrients and the lower warmer is likened to a "drainage ditch", this is the area where fluids are separated and absorbed or excreted.

The other main function of the triple warmer is to regulate the endocrine and lymphatic system.

The psychological aspect of the triple warmer is balance and harmony. The triple warmer balances the left and right side of the brain and is responsible for social expression and family ties. Socially, imbalances in this meridian may be expressed in withdrawal from or avoidance of social situations or at the other extreme of overly seeking social situations and acceptance to the neglect of home and family.

As the regulator of heat the triple warmer governs the coolness or heat of emotions. The pericardium and triple warmer as a team are believed to be responsible for perceptions and expressions of humour.

Some symptoms of general imbalance:

Inconsistencies in body temperature (e.g. hot head, cold feet), rambling thoughts, pain in the middle of the back, feeling of cold all over body, pain in temples, tendency to clench fists, heaviness in chest, stomach or torso, distress in high humidity, frequent rashes.

Psychological Qualities of Balance:

Sociable nature, ability to work well in groups, platonic friendships, personal warmth, sense of humour, liking for others.

Psychological Qualities of Imbalance:
Unsociable nature, "standoffish", lack of humour, prefers isolation to group co-operation, poor decision making abilities, forgetfulness

The Liver Meridian

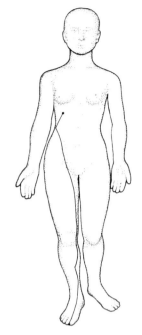

Table of Properties:

Meridian Flow:	From the inside corner of the big toe, up the inner side of the leg across to above the waist ending under the breast.
Most active time:	1.00-3.00AM
Associated Element:	Wood
Companion Organ:	Gall Bladder

LIVER FUNCTION

The function of the liver is vital to the entire body-mind and, for this reason, is sometimes referred to as the "overseer". The primary function of the liver in this regard is to ensure the smooth flow of Chi throughout the body. A tense mind and obstruction to balanced bodily functions manifest quickly if the liver is unable to successfully perform this essential task.

The second major concern of the liver is the storage of blood; the liver stores large amounts during rest and returns it for circulation when the body is active. The liver also controls the ligaments and muscular action and is directly responsible for the health of the nails.

The liver is most active during the quiet hours of the early morning when the body is at rest, at this time the liver receives a surge of energy for it's digestive functions and cleansing of the blood.

The liver is responsible for an assortment of emotional expressions with anger being the most prominent. The governing of patience comes under the control of the liver and it's partner the gall bladder - impatience is regarded as a sign of imbalance within this team.

When disturbed the liver energy reacts with aggression and shouting or with depression and also with crying of a particular type - this crying is the kind born of sheer frustration and is likened to a safety valve.

A balanced liver will show itself in impetus and forward momentum including aspirations and higher ideals; aggressive tendencies, on the other hand, reveal an imbalance of the liver energy.

Shouting is the outward expression of an imbalanced liver, but shouting will also cause further damage to the liver energy thus perpetuating the negative effect.

Some symptoms of general imbalance:

Muscle weakness, liver pain, aversion to wind, shouting, loud voice, irritability, headaches, nausea, stiff joints, insomnia (too many ideas, too much thinking), dizziness, avoidance of exercise, muscular spasms, aversion to heat, consumes excess sugar, tendency to stumble.

Psychological Qualities of Balance:

Drive, planning and starting skills, endurance, good reflexes, perseverance, spiritual enquiry and maintenance, quick and clear intellect, agreeable disposition, organizational abilities, ambition, patience, sense of well-being.

Psychological Qualities of Imbalance:
Anger, depression, impatience, short temper, hatred, jealousy, self-insistence, insecurity, attachment to strong opinions (even when wrong), power-hungry, over ambitious, controlling, cursing and shouting.

The Gall Bladder Meridian

Table of Properties:

Meridian Flow:	From the outside of the eye around the ear up and forward over the head before doubling back to travel down the body ending in the fourth toe.
Most active time:	11.00PM-1.00AM
Associated Element:	Wood
Companion Organ:	Liver

GALL BLADDER FUNCTION

The gallbladder is responsible for the storage of bile for dissolving fatty acids, it is closely connected to it's partner - the liver - imbalance in one of these organs is soon reflected in the other.

Due to their connection with the wood element, the liver and gall bladder have an energy similar to the spring season. They represent initiative and impetus, their energy pushes and promotes growth. On a psychological level the gall bladder is concerned with decision making.

"In addition to serving a beleaguered Liver as an outlet for accumulated toxicity, the Gallbladder, in my experience, plays the largest part in the disease process when decision making is an important part of the picture."

Dragon Rises, Red Bird Flies - Psychology & Chinese Medicine

Leon Hammer M.D.

When the liver and gallbladder team are thwarted in their natural expression they respond by trying to dominate or control a situation by creating emotional demands, manifesting anger or aggression, if their demands are not met deflation or depression will usually present.

Rage is the negative emotion attributed to the gall bladder. Anger is more the domain of the liver and tends to be older or of the simmering variety; whereas open wrath or rage belongs to the gall bladder - such rage always impairs the ability to make decisions and in this way the positive trait of the gall bladder (impetus and decision making) is thrown out of balance.

37

Some symptoms of general imbalance:

Nausea, gallstones, rage, anger of the sort that leads to irrational or hasty decisions, clenched fists or jaw, knee pains, allergies, bruising easily.

Psychological Qualities of Balance:

Good decision making abilities, impetus, inspiration behind decisions.

Psychological Qualities of Imbalance:
Irritability, rage, bitterness, constant sadness, impertinence.

CHAPTER 3

Elements & Emotions

ELEMENTS & EMOTIONS

Traditional Chinese Medicine documents five different ways in which the chi energy manifests and circulates throughout the universe. These five different expressions are presented as the Theory of the Five Elements: Fire, Water, Earth, Wood and Metal.

As a part of the universe, the body and mind are also considered to be subject to the rules and influences of the five elements. This theory offers a holistic view of the individual and his or her environment according to correlations with the basic elements, conditions and energies.

The five elements each have a representative climate or emotion and when viewed with their related meridian team (or teams in the case of the fire element) give great insight into the workings of the body-mind as an interdependent unit. Physiology and psychology are combined into a holistic overview of the whole person thus providing a complete and balanced healing module.

The five elements are seen as phases of a process rather than separate units. As representations of nature they relate to a number of areas (season, colour, emotion, sound, etc.) and they express these areas as part of a greater picture, part of a moving and regulating cycle.

The nourishing cycle is outlined below; this is usually depicted as a wheel or circle with one element feeding and moving on to the next around the outer rim.

The Five Elements Cycle:

Wood produces Fire (as fuel) - Fire produces Earth (as ash) -
Earth produces Metal (as ore) - Metal produces Water (by melting) -
Water produces Wood (by nourishing trees) and Wood produces Fire….

The secondary cycle is the control cycle and this shows how one element controls or subdues another.

The Control Cycle:

Wood controls the earth by penetrating it with it's roots
Earth controls Water by containing it
Water controls Fire by extinguishing it
Fire controls Metal by melting it
Metal controls Wood by chopping it...

WATER

Associated with night time and rest, the water element provides survival instinct. It's associated emotion is fear - in balance this manifests as healthy caution.

It is the source of will and provides stamina and endurance. Constitutional inheritance comes under the control of the water element in it's relationship with the kidneys which store the essence (jing).

Skills and abilities also fall under the domain of water.

WOOD

Wood is the spring element, the element of push, drive and impetus. Inspirations, ideas and beginnings are the positive focus of the wood energy. The wood element oversees metabolism both physical and mental. Decision making is the primary focus of the wood energy.

The wood element produces a grounded demeanour possessing both stamina and flexibility; when imbalanced or thwarted the wood element expresses frustration and anger both physical and mental feelings of constriction are born of disturbance to the wood element.

Dr Ted Kaptchuck author of "The Web that has no Weaver" writes of the wood element as possessing the "virtue" of human kindness - kindness, generosity and the ability to forgive are the positive qualities expressed by a strong wood influence.

FIRE

The fire element belongs to the summer season. The fire element is concerned with action and dynamism. Creativity, vision, intelligence, communications (particularly interpersonal), verbal and musical skills all fall under the domain of the fire element along with expressions of human "warmth".

Enthusiasm and a caring nature are born of a strong presence of the fire element. Love, tolerance and gentleness are also expressions of balanced fire. (See the heart meridian).

EARTH

The earth element maintains a centre position from which it can sustain and link together the other four. Earth is the element of maintenance. The stomach and spleen are the organs functioning under the control of the earth element - these organs are concerned with absorption and nurturing of the body-mind. This is where we see the transformational aspect of the earth element in action; absorption means taking something from an external source and assimilating it into something of our own.

On a physical level earth oversees the transformation of digested food into blood; and on a psychological level it is responsible for understanding and thought. Positive results come from efficient absorption - over thinking is the negative expression of earth (see notes on the spleen) and can result in a cycle or worry or even obsession if it goes unchecked. Addictions and compulsive behaviour are linked to the earth element and it's organ team. A strong and balanced earth influence facilitates the exploration of the possibilities of the mind.

METAL

The metal element in balance is concerned with the "here and now" it is the element of the present tense it provides the interface with our surroundings and experiences whereby we can take things in and also let them go.

The skin is under the jurisdiction of metal and is a good illustration of it's nature - the skin provides a boundary or container; it also absorbs and excretes - that is it has to "breathe" or take something in to survive (if the skin is entirely covered and cannot breathe the body cannot survive for long), and it also "lets go" by eliminating waste through perspiration. So the process central to the metal element is accepting and letting go.

"The Metal element reflects both the capacity to be involved and responsive as well as that of being detached and separate. It's dual nature is like the breath: expanding and contracting, receiving and releasing. It teaches us to partake of life, but without trying to "hold on to it".

Shiatsu The Complete Guide—Chris Jarmey & Gabriel Mojay

THE GREATER PICTURE

There is a direct relationship between the quality of a person's emotions and their physical health. Each meridian/internal organ is directly connected with a range of emotions— organs exert influence on the expression of particular emotions and the organ function is, in turn, affected by the expression of those emotions. In the case of negative expressions this can set up a downward spiral. For example shouting is the expression of imbalance of the liver energy or meridian - that expression means frustration and feeling thwarted has built up to the degree that it will now be expressed externally and shouting is the way the liver makes itself heard. But that shouting, as we have mentioned before, is further damaging to the liver thus perpetuating the cycle of imbalance. With this in mind, we can clearly see how the emotions play their role in the cause of disease.

The following is a summary table of the elements and meridians and their associated negative states:

ELEMENT	MERIDIAN/ORGAN	RELATED NEGATIVE EMOTIONAL STATE
FIRE	HEART	Joy– excessive, hysteria, shock
FIRE	SMALL INTESTINE	Confusion, vulnerability
FIRE	PERICARDIUM	Sadness, sorrow, instability Emotional void
FIRE	TRIPLE WARMER	Disorientation - particularly socially Suspicion
WOOD	LIVER	Repressed anger
WOOD	GALL BLADDER	Rage, internal conflict, indecision
WATER	KIDNEY	Chronic fear, sadness, insecurity
WATER	BLADDER	Memory, disappointment
METAL	LUNG	Grief
METAL	LARGE INTESTINE	Stubbornness, stagnation Holding on to past hurts
EARTH	STOMACH	Anxiety, emptiness, addiction
EARTH	SPLEEN	Self-esteem, worried thoughts

Table showing the major characteristics of the Five Elements

	WOOD	FIRE	EARTH	METAL	WATER
Direction	East	South	Centre	West	North
Season	spring	summer	long summer	autumn	winter
Climate	windy	hot summer	damp	dry	cold
Colour	green	red	yellow	white	blue/black
Yin Organ	liver	heart	spleen	lungs	kidneys
Yang Organ	gall bladder	small intestine	stomach	large intestine	bladder
Opening	eyes	tongue	mouth	nose	ears
Bodily Fluid	tears	sweat	saliva	mucous	urine
Tissue	tendons ligaments	blood vessels	muscles flesh	skin hair	bones marrow
Stage	birth	growth	transformation	harvest	storage
Taste	sour	bitter	sweet	pungent	salty
Smell	goatish	burnt	fragrant	rank	rotten
Sound	shouting	laughter	singing	weeping	groaning
Main Emotion	anger	happiness	pensiveness	sadness	fear
Reveals Condition of	nails	complexion	lips	body hair	head hair
Emotional Indications	lethargy	hysteria	worry/obsessions self-absorption	grief rejection	paranoia foolhardiness
Responsible for	control decisions	joy	compassion	letting go	ambition will power
Life Aspect	will	spirit	ideas	animal spirit	faith/courage
Personality	hard working	active	calm	simple	likes movement
Injured by excess of	walking	eye strain	sitting	lying down	standing

CHAPTER 4

An Introduction to Meridian Therapies

The Development of Present Day Meridian Therapies

Californian clinical psychologist Dr R. J. Callahan developed a unique form of meridian therapy called Thought Field Therapy. Thought Field Therapy has been in use for twenty years and is a natural non-invasive system for eradicating negative or imbalanced emotions.

Dr Callahan chose to enter the field of psychology because he had many phobias as a child and wanted to find out more about treatment methods for dealing with them. He was a pioneer in the development of clinical hypnotherapy and in the 1950s began researching any techniques that he felt would be useful in eliminating fears.

The Kinesiology Connection

Twenty years ago Dr Callahan was introduced to the concept of muscle testing by a colleague. He was amazed by the simple fact that recalling a negative thought or experience would cause an indicator muscle to weaken and took this as an excellent indication of the connection between the body and the mind.

He became fascinated by this idea and set about trying to find out everything he could. His enquiries led him to find that this discovery was the work of Dr George Goodheart the American chiropractor who was the originator of Applied Kinesiology. He began to look seriously into the history and relevance of the meridian system and began training in Applied Kinesiology.

One day, whilst working with a long-standing client with a severe phobia of water Dr Callahan decided to experiment with tapping on a key point on the stomach meridian – the resultant breakthrough, which became the foundation of the development of Thought Field Therapy, is outlined below.

Mary had a fear of water which was so intense that she could not go outside when it was raining and could not face bathing in more than a few centimetres of water. The traditional cognitive approaches of psychotherapy had assisted her to a degree but the intense fear remained. Even to watch a water scene on television would make her sick to her stomach. She had lived with this intense fear since she was a young child – when it was suggested that she ask her parents about it they confirmed that it had been present as far back as anyone could remember.

After a year and a half of using various psychotherapy techniques Mary could just about sit by a swimming pool after much coaxing but she could not look at the water.

Considering the connection between Mary's fear and they way it affected her stomach he decided to try, as an experiment, tapping on a key point on the stomach meridian found just below the eye in line with the pupil. He did not expect significant results from this and later commented:

"I was totally unprepared for what happened. As I tapped under her eye, Mary said, "It's gone, my fear of water, it's gone! I don't have those awful feelings in my stomach any more." I suggested that we go down to the swimming pool adjacent to my office to see if this was really true. I expected her to resist as usual, but in fact had to hurry to keep up with her. For the first time in her life, she bent down, put her head close to the water and began splashing it on her face."

Mary used to have nightmares about water weekly - since tapping on the stomach points she has not had another nightmare she enjoys swimming and has been on cruises – it is now 15 years since Mary was relieved of her water phobia.

Encouraged by this initial success, Dr Callahan set about trying this new discovery on all his clients and subsequently found that various combinations of points based on the 14 main meridians were extremely helpful in eliminating a wide range of negative emotions.

As a result of the observations he made when he applied his first successful treatment procedure, Dr Callahan proposed the concept of the "thought field" as the area in which the elements of psychological disturbances exist.

The theory of Thought Field Therapy asserts that if a person suffers emotional distress whilst thinking about a problem their thought field has disturbances within it. This thought field is seen as an expression of the energy system of the body. Disturbances held within that systems are responsible for the appearance of negative emotions. If the disturbance is removed from the thought field – the negative emotion is lost, or dissolved. This means that an individual is able to recall and discuss their problem with the usually accompanying distress no longer present.

Dr Callahan further refined TFT and went on to develop a series of meridian points which released varying types of negative emotions when tapped. These treatments became known as algorithms – specific sequences of tapping points for the relief of specific problems.

To this day, Kinesiology practitioners world-wide use Dr Callahan's technique for dispelling fears and phobias by simply tapping on the first point on the stomach meridian. Brian Butler co-founder of the Academy of Systematic Kinesiology writes in Balanced Health Volume One of "a frankly amazing technique discovered by a Dr Callahan, a psychologist who found that his work could be greatly enhanced with Kinesiology".

Some might comment, myself included, that the work of many kinesiologists might be greatly enhanced by the extensive research and discoveries of Dr Callahan and the advanced understanding of the mind/meridian connection that he has brought to this essential area of energy medicine.

In the course of developing this highly effective treatment method for fears and phobias, Dr Callahan also discovered a method for alleviating a major problem encountered in psychotherapy: the problem of strong negative emotions interfering with thoughts and responses in daily functioning.

From TFT to EFT

Gary Craig, one of Dr Callahan's first students, experimented further with the principles and practices of TFT and decided to streamline the process. Thus he incorporated all of the tapping points into one sequence. In this way all 14 meridian points were automatically covered in each and every application of tapping. Gary Craig called this streamlined version EFT – Emotional Freedom Techniques™. The principle in use here is that by automatically and systematically covering all of the points the need for complex diagnosis is eliminated. Since it only takes a minute or two to complete each round of tapping this makes EFT a quick, convenient and highly effective process which can be used on practically any issue or physical symptom to good effect.

How EFT Works

We have looked briefly at the theory behind TFT. Here we will look more specifically at the principles behind EFT as an advanced meridian healing method.

The common belief is that a negative emotion is the direct result of a traumatic or negative event, or memory.

MEMORY = NEGATIVE EMOTION

This proposes that all negative emotions manifest in a simple cause-effect way.

However, energy based meridian therapies offer an alternative viewpoint which rests upon a statement called "the discovery statement":

"the cause of all negative emotions is a disruption in the body's energy system"

This is indicated as follows:

MEMORY = DISRUPTION IN ENERGY SYSTEM = NEGATIVE EMOTION

This theory thus provides an intermediate step, a disruption in the energy system of the body; if the memory or event does not cause a disruption then the negative emotion cannot occur. As we are all individuals we all experience things differently - this theory clearly shows why people may show different reactions and different degrees of stress in response to what is apparently the same experience.

Therefore, rather than attempting to undo the thoughts or memories, energy based therapies, such as EFT, target this intermediate step – once the disruption in the energy system has been resolved an individual will no longer experience negative emotions or pain from the original thought or memory.

EFT does not change the memory itself - that remains fully intact and unchanged - what EFT does do is change the way you *feel* about it. This means that traumatic events can be recalled without the trauma. They become "something that happened". Objectively the person who experienced the event can say that it wasn't a good thing or even that it was "really horrible" but they don't *feel* really horrible anymore when they think or speak about it. The pounding heart, sick stomach, dizziness, intense sadness or fear or whatever other associated physical or emotional responses which may have been present at the mere mention or fleeting memory of a traumatic event are gone.

EFT puts events in their correct time frame - events from the past belong in the past. This is one of the most satisfying things I have observed when using EFT with clients and in workshops. To see someone recover a true positive present tense and step away from a piece of emotional history from years ago which had been lurking on their shoulder each and every day since it happened is amazing.

Now that we've covered some background and introduced you to your new therapeutic friend we'll get down to the learning part so that you can experience the benefits for yourself first hand.

CHAPTER 5

Learning the Basics

Step-by-Step Emotional Freedom

EFT is a process which needs to be "aimed" at a given target; we could use the example of a footballer trying to score a goal - in order to get the ball in the net he will aim it carefully in that direction. He won't just kick the ball and watch it ricochet around the pitch hoping it might eventually end up between the posts. The same applies to the meridian therapies you are learning about here - they are most effective when they are "aimed" at a particular negative emotion, problem or traumatic memory.

So the first thing that you need to do when you want to use EFT is to choose something to use it for. Let's say, for the sake of an example, that you have chosen to work on your fear of public speaking.

The next stage is to put your chosen issue into an opening statement (which we call the *set-up* when working with EFT) then you will be ready to begin tapping the fear away using a sequence of potent meridian points.

In this case your statement would be something like "Even though I have this fear of public speaking. I deeply and completely accept myself."

It is important to note here that this is not an affirmation. What we are basically saying here is "OK I have this particular problem which I'm now going to target with the intent of getting some relief". Some people have shown concern over this statement that it may be cementing in negative ideas - it isn't. This is simply proved by the fact that once the problem has been identified in this way and the EFT sequence has been tapped it will have lessened significantly in the vast majority of cases.

"Even though I have this (whatever the problem may be). I deeply and completely accept myself" is the basic opening statement formula you can use whenever you want to do some healing with EFT.

This statement is repeated three times while you rub an area on the chest called the sore spot. The sore spot is a key area known as a neuro-lymphatic reflex point - but all we really need to know about it for the purposes of EFT is that rubbing this area is important in getting us properly set-up to use the sequence to maximum effect. If you take a look at the diagram on the page 57 you will see where the sore-spot is situated.

Now you know the first stage - rub the sore spot while repeating your chosen set-up statement three times.

The next stage is to begin tapping the EFT treatment points. The easy way to do this is to tap them with your first and middle fingers with a light but firm pressure by tapping with two fingers you can be sure that you have thoroughly covered the area where the point is located.

While tapping each point about 7 times you can use what we call a "reminder phrase". The reminder phrase is a couple of words taken from your set-up statement which sums up the issue at hand for you and keeps your mind tuned in to it while the EFT sequence gets to work at giving you some relief. This is a key part of aiming your tapping at the goal as mentioned on the previous page.

In this case your words might be "fear of public speaking" it is a good idea to repeat the reminder phrase out loud as you begin to tap each point - you can say it under your breath if you find it more comfortable but vocalising it in some way is definitely helpful to the process.

Getting to Know your Healing Points

Once you have gone over the EFT points a couple of times they will start to feel familiar to you and you can get used to using them confidently for whatever you choose - below is a description of their location, along with the diagram opposite, this will give you a clear understanding of where to find them. If you want to tap each of the points as you read where they are located you can begin to learn the sequence now.

1. **Eye Brow** - at the beginning of the eyebrow, just above and to one side of the nose.
2. **Side of the Eye** - on the bone bordering the outside corner of the eye.
3. **Under Eye** - on the bone under the eye about one inch below and in line with the pupil.
4. **Under Nose** - in the centre of the area between the nose and top lip.
5. **Chin** - in the centre between the bottom lip and bottom (or point) of the chin.
6. **Collarbone** - the junction where the collarbone, sternum (breastbone) and first rib meet.
7. **Under the Arm** - on the side of the body approx. 4 inches below the armpit.
8. **Thumb** - on the outside edge of the thumb right next to the base of the thumbnail.
9. **Index Finger** - on the edge of the index finger right next to the base of the nail.
10. **Middle Finger** - on the edge of the middle finger next to the base of the nail.
11. **Baby Finger** - on the edge of the little finger next to the base of the nail.
12. **Karate Chop** - in the middle of the fleshy part on the outside of the hand.

Fig. Tapping the Under Eye point

56

Points for EFT Sequence

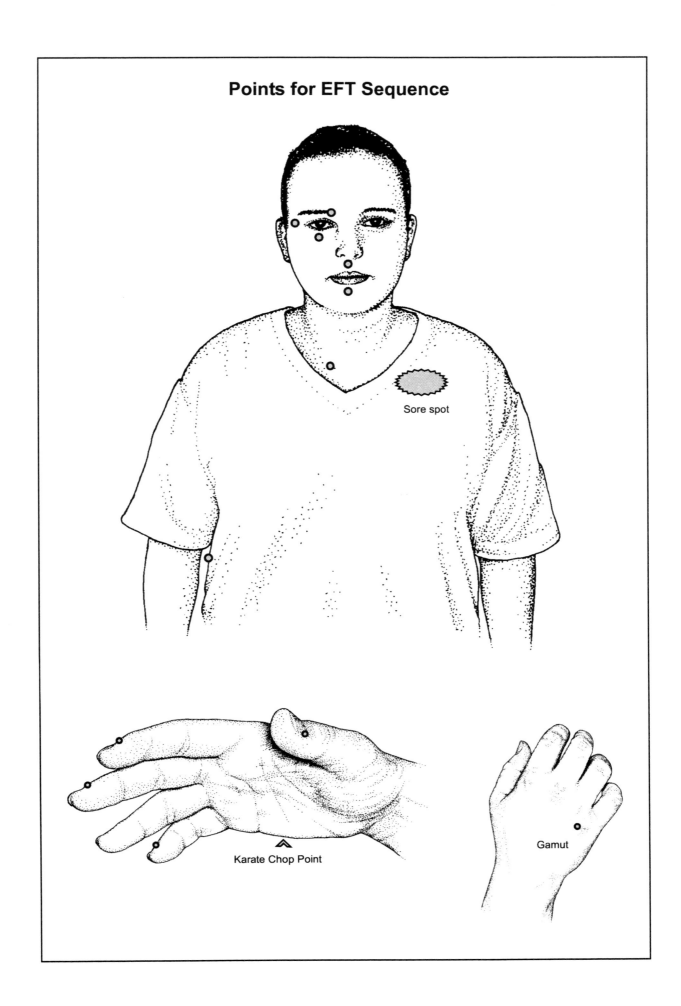

Sore spot

Karate Chop Point

Gamut

Monitoring Your Progress

When using EFT with clients we always ask them to give us an idea of how intense the issue they are presenting is for them. We call this a SUDs level - SUD stands for "Subjective Units of Disturbance" and that disturbance is rated on a scale of nought to ten. It is also useful when working with these techniques to use the SUDs scale as a way of monitoring your progress.

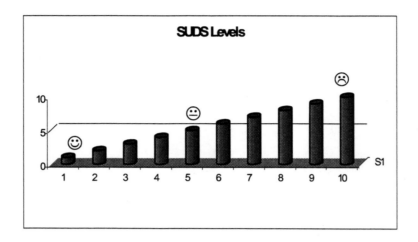

Fig. SUDS scale

The table below will give you some idea of the emotional "charge" or intensity of feeling that each number on the SUDS scale represents. Using the Emotional Freedom Technique, the aim is to reduce the SUDS level to a "0". This may require several rounds of the EFT tapping sequence and will definitely require that you remain fully focused on the issue at hand using your chosen reminder phrase to make sure that your mind doesn't wander elsewhere.

1	Calm and in control with just a hint of the problem
2	Calm and relaxed with some small awareness of the issue
3	Some slight disturbance
4	Noticeable disturbance but tolerable
5	Disturbance quite apparent and causing some discomfort
6	Disturbance is very present with obvious discomfort
7	Disturbance is very strong and very uncomfortable
8	Intense disturbance and discomfort
9	Severe disturbance and discomfort almost unbearable
10	Maximum disturbance, unbearable and all encompassing

When rating your SUDs level it is important that you assess your feelings in the present tense. If a fear of heights would be a 9 if you were standing on the edge of a cliff but is only a 4 when you are thinking about it when you're at home you should still work with the 4.

Overview of the Main Process:

1.   Choose an issue or problem that you want to work on
2.   Rate your level of disturbance over it from 1 –10.
3.   Choose your opening statement.
4.   Say it three times while rubbing the "sore-spot".
5.   Tap the EFT sequence using a reminder phrase to keep you tuned in to the problem.
6.   Take a deep breath in and let it out.
7.   Re-assess your SUDs level and repeat the process as necessary.

Once you get used to the above steps they will only take a couple of minutes to complete. You may need to repeat the process a few times depending on the nature of the issue and the number of facets related to it - the next chapter will show you how to do this.

Subsequent Rounds

Once you are satisfied that the SUDs have dropped to a much more comfortable level you can change the set-up to focus on the remaining disturbance; in this way you are tuning in to the issue again for further relief.

To do this you can say something along the lines of:

"Even though I have some remaining fear of….." or "Even though there is still some of this problem…" and repeat steps 4 to 7 above.

Finally, once the SUDs have dropped down to a 1 or 2, you can change the set-up to:

"I want to be completely free of this problem…." and repeat steps 4-7 to be completely free of the problem right down to O.

You now know how to use EFT!

Once a problem is resolved with EFT it is unlikely that you will need to repeat the procedure for it again. If some disturbance does return it will more than likely be due to another aspect coming to the surface - we will cover aspects shortly.

What if the SUDs Don't Drop?

This is a brief "trouble-shooter". If you have tapped a couple of rounds and then re-assessed the SUDs level and it hasn't dropped please take a look at the following possible reasons.

The most likely cause is that the set-up statement wasn't right, or that the problem was addressed in a way that was too broad or general. In this case the solution is to break the problem down and try again.

As mentioned previously, EFT works best when aimed at a target, in order to do that properly we need to be specific - if you are dealing with something that has a few layers or angles to it you just have to persevere and deal with one thing at a time and work through the layers - you'll be surprised at how much you can achieve in just half an hour when working with EFT in this way.

If you are still disappointed at your results after breaking a problem down and trying different set-ups please take the time to look up an experienced EFT practitioner. I am convinced that EFT works - it has a very high success rate. That success rate, however, is sometimes dependant on a little experience and detective work!

Here's a recent case that I was presented with of EFT not working: after a huge argument a client of mine tapped for her hurt feelings, she later told me that "it didn't work at all". I asked her what set-up she had used and she told me "Even though I'm upset..." and then carried on to say "but it didn't work because I was too angry to even think straight".

What do you think might have happened if she'd used EFT for the anger first and then gone on to deal with her hurt feelings afterwards?

A Word of Caution

It sometimes happens that when somebody is newly introduced to EFT that they will try it out on something that has been bothering them for years and find that within a few minutes the severity of the problem has been greatly reduced. It may have been causing them a disturbance which they rated 7 out of 10 and then dropped to around a 3 out of 10 after a couple of rounds of tapping. That is a likely scenario and is obviously a good thing rather than a problem.

However, it may become a problem if, having experienced comparative relief, you chose to go on to another issue, and then another, and another leaving them all at around a level 3 or 4. Some people who have done this have eventually found themselves feeling somewhat overwhelmed with several issues all at level 3 or 4 vying for attention. Several unsettled 3 or 4's can soon start adding up to bigger numbers again.

Obviously, an issue that was a 9 or 10 will feel much relieved when reduced to a 3 or 4. But how much better still would it feel if each issue where settled at a 1 before moving to the next. That is the best method for working with EFT, to be thorough and methodical. Focus on one issue at a time and deal with it fully before moving on to the next.

EFT is such a tool that once you have mastered it and become familiar, through experience, with how it works you can be confident that with a little intuition and careful application the vast majority of emotional disturbances can be successfully "laid to rest" at zero permanently. The key to maximum relief here is persistence.

CHAPTER 6

Putting it Into Practice

Your First EFT Experience

The following is a guided exercise intended to give you a tangible experience with EFT while getting used to using the process.

TENSION RELEASE EXERCISE

On a scale of 1 to 10 how tense do you feel right now? Are you aware of any areas of tension in your body? Give it some consideration and pick a number as your SUDs level for this exercise.

Now find the sore spot and rub it while repeating out loud three times:

"Even though I have this tension I deeply and completely accept myself."

Next—find the Eyebrow Point and tap on it about seven times and say "this tension".

Now the Side of the Eye point - tap and say "this tension"

Under the Eye - "this tension"

Under the Nose - "this tension"

Chin - "this tension"

Collar Bone - "this tension"

Under the Arm - ...

Thumb ...

Index Finger ...

Middle Finger ...

Little Finger ...

And Karate Chop point ...

Now take a big deep breath in and release it. How tense do you feel now? If it was a 4 before, for example, what is it now?

You should now have some idea of the usefulness of EFT and have some idea of how to get a SUDs level on an issue and put the technique into practice for it.

This is a useful exercise that you can use at any time. If you don't like the words used here you can choose your own "Even though I feel really tense/wound up/irritated/fed up..." whatever you like; these techniques always work best with your own words - your words make sense to you and can immediately sum up your feelings.

As you use EFT more and more you will become more familiar with your thoughts and emotions and will find that it gets easier for you to get in touch with yourself and isolate issues for attention. We will cover an exercise to help you with this shortly.

Now that you are familiar with the EFT treatment sequence we can begin to look at putting the technique into practice.

Approaches

The approaches we will cover here will be greatly beneficial in tuning in to problems and finding the right set-up statement. They will also give you a greater understanding of the variety of ways in which EFT can be used.

One important thing to remind you of here is that only you know the right words to describe how you feel or what your problems mean to you. Grammar and logic are of no value when choosing a set-up statement the only thing that matters is that the words mean something to you and have a degree of emotional intensity that is relevant to the issue at hand.

EFT deals with "calling a spade a spade" it is designed to deal with real people expressing real emotions. Therefore if you have a fear of spiders, for example, and would say that you are "bloody terrified of spiders", or that "spiders horrible legs make me feel sick" and you shift in your seat or shudder as you say it then those are the words you should use for the set-up. You can experiment here and you will see that in such a case that an objective "my spider phobia" statement won't get the job done in the quite the same way, in fact it may not do anything at all. Real feelings for real relief.

The Statement Approach

The first, and perhaps most commonly used approach is the statement approach - this is where you simply name the problem and then tap a round, or rounds, of EFT for it.

The basic statement is "Even though I (*insert problem here…*) I deeply and completely accept myself".

Here are some examples for this approach to give you some ideas of the variety of issues you can use it for:

"Even though I have this fear of mice…"

"Even though I want to eat all the time…"

"Even though I feel disgusted with myself…"

"Even though I have this stiffness in my neck…"

"Even though I'm so worried about…"

"Even though I have no confidence…"

I often use this straightforward approach with clients and in our personal development workshops and have seen many times the amazement on people's faces as they are released from the grip of long-standing limitations.

One lady who attended a workshop a few months ago recently called in to our centre and told me "You remember my driving phobia? Well, it's completely gone – I've been saving up and I'm on my way to buy a car right now."

At our *Building Bridges to a Brighter Future* workshop we ask everyone to choose a negative core belief that they would like to change (i.e. be free from). Recently two ladies in the same group stated that they "didn't feel good enough" they both said that this was a very strong feeling for them and rated it at ten out of ten. Fifteen minutes later they both reported that this was no longer true - one of them was actually looking around the room to see where the feeling had gone! I have spoken with them several times since the workshop and they both assure me that five months later the positive change they experienced is still effective and that they are more confident and in touch with their resources and abilities.

Investigating Root Causes

This approach is used to try and pinpoint the underlying cause of an issue and target it for positive change. EFT is very useful when used in this way as it often provides some insight to the issue at hand.

The set-up statement used for this approach would be something like "Even thought I don't know why I have (*this problem…*)".

When EFT is used in this way it will often bring to the surface memory flashes or thoughts and ideas about the problem, body sensations that are triggered by the issue, or specific feelings and emotional responses. Take careful note of anything that comes to light here.

"Even though I have this… memory/dizziness/sadness…" Whatever comes up you can use for the next set up statement and subsequent round of tapping to get to the root of the problem.

The Trigger Approach

The trigger approach can be used with anything that "triggers" a negative memory or emotion. Practically *anything* can be a potential trigger; a sound, a smell, a flower, music, a place, a word…

Think back to the discovery statement - something somewhere causes a disruption in the energy system and the recall of that memory is accompanied by a whole host of emotions and sensations instantly. Talking about it or thinking about it even for a fleeting moment will bring the whole thing rushing back with it's entire entourage of associated feelings.

Triggers do the same. And for that very reason people will often consciously avoid them.

However, when combined with EFT triggers serve as a very effective and thorough inroad for emotional clearance.

Some examples of trigger approaches are: films, photographs, music, objects & substances.

To give an example - somebody with a fear of flying could select a film with airport and flight scenes in it and tap the EFT sequence for whatever the film brings up for them. They can watch a selected scene over a few times and systematically deal with their discomfort or negative feelings until they are able to watch the scene through and feel completely comfortable with it.

The disturbance experienced when watching the film is directly related to that *disruption in the energy system* which is the underlying cause of the fear of flying; therefore, the core of the issue can be effectively resolved using this method.

To give another example of using triggers with EFT: A client recently approached me with a strong fear of returning to employment after a long period at home. During the course of our discussion he mentioned that even seeing job advertisements in the newspaper would trigger a feelings of panic and guilt.

We used EFT during the session for the negative emotions he identified and I also suggested that over the next few days he went through the papers and looked over the job advertisements and tapped with EFT for whatever came up. Once all the fears and objections to calling for an interview had been resolved and the panic had gone there was nothing to stop him applying for work.

EFT is such an effective tool when used in this way that huge relief is experienced and people will actually seek out the activity that they had previously feared or avoided.

The trigger approach can be experimented with in a variety of ways - however, caution should be exercised at all times. Never expose yourself to triggers which may cause a severe reaction - if you are in any doubt seek out a licensed Meridian Therapy practitioner who is trained to guide you safely through the process.

"Adventures in EFT" by Silvia Hartmann is an excellent source of information on working with EFT in this way.

The Story Approach

The story approach is a good way to recall and clear a disturbing memory or incident.

In order to use the story approach start your tale a little before the event you wish to clear. Observe yourself carefully as you begin to speak and you will notice the first word or phrase which reveals a charge or emotional disturbance. Having found the first word or phrase that shows up a disturbance you can incorporate it in the set-up statement and use the EFT sequence for it until you can repeat that part of the story with no sign of a disturbance over it.

You can then continue on to the next part of your story stopping each time you feel some emotional intensity and tapping for each phrase or word that pinpoints it. Once you are done you should be able to recall the entire incident freely and tell your story without feeling any disturbance over it.

Here follows an example of using EFT with the story approach this is a transcript used with the permission of a client whose house had been burgled:

"I came back from the pictures and (pause, sharp intake of breath) my front door was open"

The pause and change in breathing indicate that the words that follow are significant.

We tapped for: "Even though my front door was open…"

(This is an effective statement because the client was well aware of what "the door being open" meant to them at that time and the sensations it brought when those words were used.)

Once they were able to repeat that part of the story without hesitation or a change in their breathing or body posture they were ready to continue with their story.
"My door was open" (no emotion) "and I could see my CD's (change in voice and facial expression) on the floor in the hall"

To the detached observer it is obvious that the first indication that something was "wrong" was seeing the door open and then to see the CD's on the hall floor was the unwelcome confirmation that someone had been in the house - again here the words of the clients story are perfectly sufficient to eliminate the related disturbance.

We used EFT with: "Even though my CD's where on the floor…".

We continued in this way until the whole story could be retold without the client experiencing any degree of disturbance.

Always check when using EFT in this way that you are completely comfortable with the story now. Any residual feelings of discomfort can be quickly eliminated using the same approach. Again, it's just a question of being thorough and persistent.

EFT is so effective when properly applied that "better" is not good enough - "better" means comparative relief; with perseverance and careful attention we can strive for the presenting problem being "completely gone". An experienced EFT practitioner is always looking for that amazed expression a person will manifest when they feel complete relief.

The Stepping Stone Approach

This is the ideal approach for dealing with a long-standing problem where you may not feel comfortable with the repercussions that immediate freedom may bring either to yourself, or your friends and relatives.

The stepping stone approach is a safe and effective way of resolving the problem step-by-step over a period of time thus allowing for a gradual adjustment for all involved.

Gentle change one step at a time is less frightening for many people. It is often the case in long standing conditions that there is a fear of change or recovery; often it seems easier to struggle on with "the devil we know" than adopt a positive change. Using this approach the fear can be eased as progress is made.

Any other conscious objections to the process of change can also be eased away using this approach. If you are not sure where to begin you can ask yourself how would I feel if I knew I could be rid of this... (problem) tomorrow?

Would you feel afraid? Apprehensive? Under pressure from the expectations of others? Or even from yourself? Any nagging concerns can be gradually dissolved at your own pace over whatever period of time you choose. EFT is a very flexible process.

Pre-Problem Solving

Pre-problem solving tapping is another gentle and extremely thorough approach. It is a useful way of dealing with any objections to progress that may arise. Larry Nims Ph.D. the developer of BSFF™ calls this "stopping stoppers".

In his BE SET FREE FAST™ Manual he writes: "You may well discover a great deal of personal resistance within yourself as you start to do these treatments for yourself. Resistance is just another term for various combinations of subconscious programming, fear, lack of confidence, low self-image and a variety of learned "stoppers" – all operating outside of your conscious awareness."

These "stoppers" are our objections to positive change if somebody is overweight and contemplating a weight loss program their "stopper" may be "I haven't got the will power."

If they tap a round for "Even though I haven't got the willpower..." their belief will change – they will no longer believe they haven't got the will power and may well decide to have a go at following a program. They may well have other objections of course; the simple solution there is more of the same – "Even though I can't resist cakes..." whatever comes up can be tapped down.

I have used this method many times with clients, one had been dieting happily for some time and then came to me feeling that they couldn't possibly continue (their words). We talked about it for a bit and after a few minutes they told me that they couldn't believe that their body would ever look nice again after being overweight for so long so what would be the point in continuing?

We tapped for "Even though I don't believe my body will ever look nice..."

And they felt greatly relieved and continued with their chosen regime.

Pre-problem solving is excellent for use with issues of personal identity, possibility, motivation etc.

These are issues that are often identified as "Psychological Reversals" (which we will cover shortly). More often than not these things are the real reason behind problems.

"I don't deserve to get over this."
"It's not possible for me to be free of this."
"I'm afraid to overcome this."

These are common statements that come up around problems and once they are quieted the real healing process can begin.

Using this approach you can ask yourself "How do I feel about having this problem?" Once your feelings and objections to the positive alternative are identified you can start to apply the EFT protocol and change them.

"Even though I don't deserve to get over this. I deeply and completely accept myself."
"Even though it's not possible for me to be free of this. I deeply and completely accept myself."
"Even though I'm afraid to overcome this problem. I deeply and completely accept myself."

Non-Directive Tapping

Non-directive tapping means tapping the EFT sequence while not tuned in to a specific issue. Instead of choosing a set-up statement identifying a problem you can simply say "I deeply and profoundly accept myself" while rubbing the sore spot.

You can use non-directive tapping several times a day; it is extremely effective for reducing stress, pain, depression and boosting your immune system. Using EFT in this way is particularly useful if you are feeling "swamped" or overwhelmed and just don't know where to begin with the process of getting some relief.

Psychological Reversals - The Inner Battle

The concept of the psychological reversal has provided a major breakthrough in the understanding and resolving of emotional and physical pain. Have you ever begun a weight loss programme, or exercise regime and abandoned it a couple of weeks later, or set into motion positive intentions which have soon come to nothing?

If you have – you are not alone.

Many people berate themselves for their lack of willpower or resolve and many more are berated by others for the same. Psychological Reversal is more often than not at the root of the problem and is responsible for most situations where will power or resolve appear to be lacking. Psychological reversal is often referred to as a kind of self-sabotage, a negative state where "motivation operates in a way that is directly opposed to the way it should work" (Callahan & Perry 1991).

When we are subjected to shock or stress our natural energy flow becomes disturbed and may be come "reversed" – when this happens our body sets about fighting against its own healing resources.

"When you are psychologically reversed your actions are contrary to what you say you want to do. You might say that you want to quit eating when you aren't hungry, and in your heart of hearts you really do want to quit overeating. But in reality you are continuing to overeat. You are sabotaging your own efforts, you feel helpless and you don't know why."
(Callahan & Perry, 1991)

This theory answers questions that many healthcare practitioners have been asking themselves for years. Why is it that some people can't make any progress on the path to recovery? Why do people with potential, ability and desire to succeed in a given field repeatedly fail? Why is it that an individual will express a desire for positive change but then appear to go all out to avoid or even spoil it? Why are some people so persistently negative? Or contrary? Or "cutting their nose off to spite their own face"? Answer: Psychological Reversal (PR)- the inner battle and real reason behind most of our struggles.

The good news is that PR is easily detected and corrected. Once identified and addressed we can enjoy new healing possibilities that may have previously been unavailable to us. EFT has a PR correction built in to the sequence you have already learned.

EFT addresses specific psychological reversals when we make our set-up statement and it corrects those reversals long enough for the tapping sequence to do it's job to maximum effect unhindered by our objections to progress be they conscious or otherwise.

The PR correction built in to EFT is ideal for most situations. However, if you are not getting substantial results on a given issue it might be a good idea to ask yourself "How do I feel about having this problem?" You can then use the Pre-Problem Solving approach if you want to really get to the bottom of it.

Do you feel that you have the motivation to deal with it?

If not you can tap on the karate chop point for an alternative set-up and say "Even though I don't have the motivation to deal with this...". After doing this you can tap a round or two of EFT for this.

Are you afraid of the change and what it will mean to you?

"Even though I'm afraid to get over this..." (While tapping karate chop point)
(see "A Word About Fear" on the next page.)

Do you think you would feel deprived if you got over this problem?

If so tap the karate chop point and say: "Even though I'll feel deprived if I get over this..."

Are you afraid you may lose your identity? Or are you afraid of putting yourself in a vulnerable position because you feel you will lose a long standing method of dealing with this problem? This is where the Stepping Stone approach excels for gradual and gentle progress.

You can also address it by tapping the karate chop point and saying: "Even though I'll lose my identity if I get over this...".

You can experiment with EFT - the worst you can expect is little or no result. Each round only takes a couple of minutes so there is a very small investment of time to see if you are heading in the right direction. If one statement doesn't work then try another.

Physical symptoms are also a useful way of getting through to emotional issues - EFT practitioners often work in this way. A client may say that they have a light-headed feeling, or a pounding heart that is connected to their feelings about an issue. Tapping for *"Even though I feel dizzy..."* (or whatever the sensation may) be reduces the physical sensation and will usually also result in a drop in the SUDs level of the emotional issue too. You can easily try this for yourself - simply identify any physical sensation that you experience in connection with a particular issue and incorporate it into the set-up statement. You may find the exercise on page 79 useful for using EFT in this way.

I was recently working with a client on an anxiety issue, after a few minutes she told me "my mouth feels really strange" and so we used that statement for our next set-up - *"even though my mouth feels really strange....* At the end of that next round of tapping her bemused expression turned to surprise and she told me that the strange feeling in her mouth had completely gone - and the anxiety had gone too.

A Word about Fear

The fear we will speak about here is not of the fear of flying, water etc type. It is a very specific version of fear - fear of letting go. That is, fear of what will happen to us if we release something that we have carried around for so long that we feel it has become a part of us - albeit a negative and painful part. This is something I have encountered on several occasions with clients who have realised the potential of EFT and have made the courageous decision to tackle a big issue with it. They may be fearful of there being a big part of them missing, losing a coping tactic, what they'll be free to do without it, or just plain afraid to tackle it. In a sense, it could be said that this kind of fear comes under the category of psychological reversals.

However we label it and whatever the cause, there is one sure way to deal with it and that is to make it our first tapping sequence - tap for the fear.

"Even though I am terrified of getting over this I deeply and completely accept myself."

Once the fear of recovery is gone then the real recovery can start.

CHAPTER 7

Emotional Freedom & Choice

Validation of Emotions

If you take a group of people and ask them how they feel about certain issues or traumatic memories it will seldom be the case that any two people will give the same reply. You would expect to find empathy within the group due to a common ground and some similarities but there will also be a wide range of different responses. As individuals we react very individually to apparently similar issues and situations.

One of the main areas of complaint in interpersonal relationships is that one person may think that their feelings are not valued by another. People often say "I know it sounds silly, but that's how I feel". In other words, "I may consciously accept that it seems illogical but it makes me feel this way and that's that." Feelings are what count for most of us.

Meridian Therapies excel in dealing with feelings. According to dictionary definition, the words feeling and emotion mean pretty much the same thing, therefore we can expect emotional freedom to equate with freedom from feelings that are unpleasant or uncomfortable to us in some way.

It is a well documented fact that once a negative emotion or feeling is acknowledged and accepted in some way the process of releasing it can begin. With EFT this is a simple and dignified process, we do not need to justify and explain the feelings we have and the way things affect us, we simply have to state the facts "if I think of that it makes me feel completely sick to my stomach". If that's how you feel - then that's how you feel.

I have had people in workshops say that they feel disgusted with themselves and not good enough, one even said "I just want to rip my face off" and it was obvious by the way she said it that she really meant it. Everyone in the group wanted to say "No!" and try and make her feel better about herself. It's our natural instinct - such things are painful to say and painful to hear. But, unfortunately, kind words and cajoling are more likely to make the person suffering love you more for your thoughtfulness than themselves; there may be some temporary relief but our perceived "truths" soon return as big and ugly as ever given a little time.

With EFT rapid relief is available from the most heartbreaking outpourings. The girl mentioned above no longer felt like that after just 3 minutes of tapping! She has called me since and told me that she really doesn't feel like "ripping her face off" anymore and has set about decorating her flat and making her surroundings more to her "new" liking.

According to the energy understanding of the body/mind and the meridian system something, sometime, somewhere caused a disruption in the body's energy system and this

77

negative emotion or feeling is a result of it. The only thing an EFT practitioner needs to know about that particular feeling is whether you might feel a whole lot better without it. And if the answer is "yes" then you can get to work and be free of it.

I mentioned that EFT was a dignified process, one of the key areas where this shines through is in issues of a particularly delicate or personal nature. EFT is an exceptional therapy for sexual abuse issues. I have actually cleared a client of a childhood abuse issue without even knowing they had been abused, until they chose to tell me at the end of the session (they also told me that prior to the EFT treatment they would not have been able to talk about it). We tapped for feelings of "deep sadness" "anger" "betrayal" and more until the client said she felt fully relieved. That's dignified. It's often the case that the last thing a person wants to do with issues of that nature is talk about them and mentally drag themselves through the experience again.

I have often heard counsellors, psychotherapists and hypnotherapists comment that they will often see a client for their first session and consider it to be a thorough and successful consultation yet they know that when that person leaves their office it is unlikely that they will return for their next session. Why? Because they know that their next appointment would mean "getting down to the nitty gritty" and for a lot of people that's just too painful. They may feel that a scab has been knocked off a wound and they will be left feeling exposed and vulnerable for a period of time. This doesn't happen with EFT and for this reason these meridian therapies are often referred to as the "tearless trauma techniques".

Personal Awareness Exercise

The vast majority of people spend their lives on "auto-pilot" and in a state of constant tension. Meridian Therapies give us the opportunity to exercise more conscious control over our feelings and responses. The following exercise is designed to make you more aware of how you respond emotionally and physically to stress and external influences.

This exercise is a useful way to further develop your individual abilities for dealing with day to day work and personal relationships. We often use this exercise in our workshops as a way of targeting and relieving key areas of tension and discontent.

Think about how you respond to the following. Also try and observe your reactions to different situations over the next few days and see if there are any that you would like to change.

What happens to you when you feel frustrated or irritated?

How do you hold your body when you are working?

Is it different to when you are relaxing at home? And if so how?

If you are worried or anxious what physical sensations do you experience?

How do you feel or respond if someone is angry with you?

How do you feel about confrontations? Do you get a particular body sensation when you are confronted?

How do you feel when recalling memories about different people who are close to you?

How do you feel about past illnesses or accidents?

If you would like to change the way you deal with particular situations then you can easily and effectively do so using EFT.

"Even though I feel threatened by confrontations…"

If you no longer feel threatened by confrontations - and you won't if you use EFT in this way, then you can get in touch with your resources for dealing with confrontational situations in a way which is more to your liking. Emotional Freedom facilitates choice.

"The choices we make in present time are influenced by the traumas and joys we have experienced in the past. Choices we make today, of course, create our future. If we can defuse the traumas from the past, and reinforce the joys, we'll be making choices which create the kind of future we really want to have."
Tools of the Trade (Three in One Concepts) - Gordon Stokes & Daniel Whiteside

EFT is, in my experience, the perfect tool for dissolving the influence of past traumas. We have a tendency to develop "coping mechanisms" in response to unpleasant past experiences. Usually they are restrictive; such as avoiding any situation which could lead to a reoccurrence, or adopting a certain "exterior" - a face to convey our defensive message to the outside world.   We might deny that the event ever happened, or we might spend years consciously pushing it away from our memory and mind, distracting ourselves constantly from ever having to think about it or "deal" with it.

These ways of coping cause stress and tension which may be held in the system for years and, regrettably, often lead to health problems of one kind or another. EFT offers the bright alternative of quick and painless release.

Beliefs and Our World View

"Belief is perhaps the most potent and dynamic word in the English language. Belief is the "magic" ingredient of success. Intelligence and ability are certainly necessary - but it is belief that can carry you to the farthest and most exciting areas of life. It can demolish barriers, break down restrictions and allow one to travel just as far as one wants to go. With belief, all things are possible, all doors are open."
Allen Carmichael - Believe You Can!

For most of us our "beliefs" are our reality - good or bad. EFT can be used to fortify our positive beliefs, fan the spark of our faint but hopeful beliefs and completely change any negative beliefs you choose.

How Much are You Willing to Believe a Good Thing?

You can use EFT to install a positive belief gradually tapping to increase how much you believe it to be true. For this we use an alternative to the SUDs scale. This is called the VOC scale and it stands for Validity of Cognition - in other words "how much do you believe it". The VOC scale works in the opposite direction to the SUDs starting with a low number and building up.

For example, if you are using EFT to build your confidence you can first assess how confident you feel out of ten. If it is a two or a three, for example, you can then tap a round or two of EFT and see how many points it has increased and then continue until you feel fully confident.

Dissolving Negative Core Beliefs with EFT

We all have them to a greater or lesser degree. Those things told to us when we were children usually by someone in authority - a parent, teacher, aunt or uncle, Sunday school teacher - whoever. An adult or adults held in respect who decided to impart a pearl or two of "wisdom" to us.

"Children should be seen and not heard."

"You can't trust anyone."

"You'll never amount to much."

"You're stupid/clumsy/irresponsible..."

"The trouble with you is you've got no confidence..."

Lies told to us as children become our truths as adults. We tend to adopt them as our reality and we carry out our lives according to the limitations they impose upon us.

An example: I used to know a boy who was told repeatedly by his father that he was clumsy and irresponsible. The boy worked for the family business and his father would often recall to others in front of him his latest "clumsy" or "irresponsible" action.

As that boy entered his 20s he became more and more dejected and set in motion a chain of "irresponsible" events and eventually developed a "drink problem" - to the further dismay of his father.

When asked about his troubles and the debts he had built up he replied that he could do no better - he'd never been able to take responsibility for anything - it was just the way he was.

Dissolving negative core beliefs is an excellent area for EFT. In a matter of minutes I have seen people shrug off limitations that had coloured their lives for years. Remember the lady who felt "ten out of ten not good enough" at a workshop - that was her belief for over 20 years. After just three minutes of tapping with EFT she said it was no longer true.

As an exercise you could pick any negative or restricting belief you choose and dissolve it with EFT.

"Even though I've got no confidence..." just choose something you'd like to change. Assess how much you believe it out of ten - the SUDs level - then tap for it and watch the SUDs level drop - keep going until it is no longer true. Then start getting used to the freedom that your positive alternative offers you!

CHAPTER 8

Specific Applications

Reducing Physical Pain with EFT

For the most part, we have looked at the possibilities that EFT provides for reducing emotional suffering. In this chapter we will look at how EFT can be used in exactly the same way as you have already learned for the purpose of reducing physical pain.

Since the two are very much connected according to the theories of traditional Chinese medicine and the functioning of the meridian system you will often find that working with EFT on physical pain will reduce negative emotions and vice versa.

EFT practitioners will often switch between physical and emotional set up statements when working with clients as an effective way of lowering the SUDs at the core of the issue gently and thoroughly.

As with all problems we experience physical pain results from a disruption in the flow of vital energy around our meridian system. Oriental medicine presents several methods for reducing pain by either stimulating or sedating specific related meridians following a diagnostic procedure. Kinesiology also offers techniques for reducing pain by isolating the meridian or meridians and then using one of a few techniques available to reduce the pain.

Here, once again, the simplicity of EFT shines through and gets to work immediately on the issue at hand by addressing all of the meridians in one sequence while tuned in to the problem thus eliminating the need for diagnostic procedures.

The next time you have a headache instead of reaching for the painkillers why not try EFT? Most painkillers take about 20-30 minutes before they begin to work - EFT starts right away there's a good chance you'll be finished within 10 minutes and feeling a whole lot better.

To use EFT for physical pain relief simply assess it and choose a number on the SUDs scale that best fits it's degree of intensity then choose your set-up statement to describe it:

"Even though I have this headache/sinus pain (however you choose to label it)... I deeply and completely accept myself."

Repeat the statement a couple more times and then begin tapping a round saying "headache" or whatever you choose at each point.

At the end of the round take a deep breath in and then release it and re-assess your SUDs level and continue until you feel relieved.

Remember to use the subsequent round set ups as described on page 59 for "remaining pain" etc. until you are satisfied that you are comfortable.

Pain has a habit of changing shape or moving around when we target it for relief. If that is your experience just stick with it. Whatever the sensation changes to use a description of it for your set-up. And wherever it moves to, again use that in your set-up. This is called "chasing the pain" and the idea is to notice the changes in the pain and tap for each new one as it arises until each part of the pain is relieved .

In my experience of using EFT for tension headaches I have on several occasions experienced almost immediate relief from the headache (within under a minute) which is quickly followed by an intense pressure and heaviness across the tops of my shoulders, I would then tap for the heaviness in my shoulders; and it would move to my arms - they became so heavy that it felt hard to continue tapping.

Within two or three minutes I have been free of the headache and following heaviness and able to carry on with whatever I needed to do where previously I would have been very uncomfortable for several hours and usually have resorted to painkillers.

Rapid Relief

Dr Roger Callahan, the originator of Thought Field Therapy, has devised a shortcut sequence for dealing with pain which is useful in obtaining relief in the majority of cases.

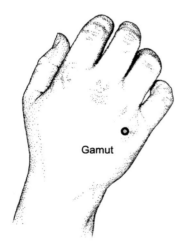

Gamut

To use this procedure:

1. Locate the "gamut" point on the back of your hand (as Illustrated here) and tap it lightly but firmly with the first two fingers of your other hand 30-50 times.

2. Now locate the Collar Bone point you use when you are tapping the EFT points and tap on that point in the same way 30-50 times.

3. Return to the gamut point and tap again 30-50 times.

Fears & Phobias

Fears and phobias vary greatly in intensity from mild unease to intense fear, which may also manifest physical symptoms such as sweating, shuddering, nausea and panic.

One in ten people suffer with a phobia which, when triggered, results in an intensely unpleasant experience. Phobias may result from a past traumatic experience, childhood frights or conditioning, they may be carried over from past lives, or they can just appear to spring from nowhere.

A real advantage of using meridian therapies for freedom from phobias is that you really don't need to know where the phobia came from to eliminate it. Many other therapies in this field would first need to ascertain the origin or cause before they could begin a program of eradication. Other treatment methods would involve desensitisation - beginning with imagining a situation and working through that until it feels more tolerable, then being gradually introduced to the actual subject of the phobia and going through each level of fear until it may be found tolerable.

For many the thought of going through this procedure for a strong phobia is a terrifying prospect. In fact, most clients who have approached me because they have a phobia have wanted to be clear from the start that they would not be exposed to the very thing they dreaded as part of the treatment before they would even consider booking an appointment.

It is clear that for someone with a spider phobia even thinking about a spider is enough to make them physically squirm. Why? It's that disruption in the energy system again.

The very thought or mention of the word is usually enough to trigger a host of unpleasant feelings and physical sensations. And for the purposes of EFT that's enough to set the process in motion.

Once again, perseverance is the key to success. It is often the case with phobias that there may be many aspects to the problem. Once the SUDs have dropped at the thought of a still spider they may shoot up again at the thought of a moving spider, or it's legs, or eyes, or speed etc. It may be that several rounds have to be tapped for a few different angles to the problem.

Once a phobia has been dissolved with EFT it should be laid to rest permanently.

Habits & Addictions

This section is designed to give you an idea of the ways in which meridian therapies can be used for freedom from addictions.

Bad habits are defined as any repeated behaviour that leads us to do something that is "not good" for us such as smoking cigarettes, overeating, hair pulling, or nail biting etc. The dictionary definition of addiction is stated as a condition which arises from having formed a habit of a particular behaviour, or become dependant on a particular substance.

Common substance addictions are: alcohol, cigarettes and both prescription and "recreational" drugs.

Whatever the nature of the habit or addiction EFT can be used to provide relief from cravings and anxiety. If you would like professional assistance with an addiction please see the resources section of this book where you will find information on how to find a licensed practitioner.

Dr Roger Callahan believes that addictions or bad habits mask an underlying emotion and that anxiety is the underlying cause of all addictions.

Since EFT is extremely effective in providing relief from anxiety we can expect it to be valuable in the treatment of addictions. EFT can be used to reduce the craving for a given substance, or behavioural urges whilst simultaneously treating the underlying anxiety.

If you think back to the section on psychological reversals (those hidden conflicts that often prevent us from achieving our goals) you can see how psychological reversal can be a major factor in failed attempts to overcome an addiction. As EFT effectively corrects reversals in addition to reducing anxiety and cravings it provides the perfect approach to freedom from habits and addictions.

It is for many the hardest thing in the world to "give up" something that has been their habit for years. For many the mere thought of "stopping smoking" or going on a "diet" will only serve to increase their smoking or eating because it increases their anxiety.

If you want to use EFT for freedom from a habit or addiction one thorough and gentle way of doing it is to use the pre-problem solving approach as described on page 70 before you even attempt to "give up" a substance or habit.

Using the pre-problem solving approach in this way means that you will be well prepared and not dependant on willpower alone once you begin your actual program.

Preparation Work

Using the pre-problem solving approach think about the following:

- *How motivated do you feel to overcome your addiction?*

- *What are your feelings about your addiction?*

- *Do you have any doubts over whether you will succeed? Or that you lack motivation?*

- *Do you have any worries about your identity?*

- *Do you doubt your willpower?*

- *Do you feel afraid or anxious about giving up your addiction?*

Note your responses to the above and treat them using EFT in the way you have already learned.

Making EFT a Habit

A very useful way of making progress in obtaining freedom from "bad habits" is to make a habit out of EFT. One particularly effective way of doing this is to tap a round of EFT for your craving or anxiety several times a day - you could use the following cues to remind you or you could make some of your own.

- *When you go to bed at night*

- *When you get up in the morning*

- *Before each meal*

- *After each meal*

- *Every time you enter the bathroom*

If your watch has an hourly chime you could also use that as a reminder. Since each round of EFT only takes a minute or two it is very easy to incorporate EFT into your daily routine in this way with minimal interruption and for maximum benefit.

In addition to using EFT at set times of the day you can use it "on the spot" for relief from cravings. Whenever the desire arises you can quickly and easily reduce it using EFT.

For example, if you are following a weight loss program and you are desperate for a bar of chocolate you can use the EFT process until your desire is tapped away and you no longer want it.

You can also use EFT to focus your attention on any withdrawal symptoms you may be experiencing and see if you can reduce them by tapping as well.

As always when working with EFT it is helpful to try and be a little thoughtful about the process - you will soon get used to this with a little practise. It simply means getting into the habit of asking yourself "How do I feel about this?".

EFT & Weight Loss

"We eat when we're glad and we eat when we're sad - especially when we're sad."

James Durlacher - Freedom from Fear Forever

We can't avoid eating not only is it essential to our survival but it is also a central part of our social life. And advertising and marketing don't help us when food products are endorsed as comforting and emotionally supportive. Many people live to eat rather than eating to live.

Logically enough the stomach meridian is connected with all issues of digestion and weight control. If you refer back to the information on the stomach meridian on page 20 you will see that addictions are directly related to an imbalance of the stomach energy.

One of the hardest areas to deal with when controlling our eating patterns is an "emptiness" or feeling of constant hunger. Many of us eat way beyond the point of satisfying our natural appetite because we are looking for more from our food than mere sustenance—rather than nutritional support we are looking for emotional support.

An understanding of the psychological perspective of the meridians clearly shows how imbalances manifest in this way. EFT automatically addresses these imbalances and facilitates a change of dietary habits in the same gentle yet thorough way that it addresses so many other problems

If want to use EFT in this way you can start by finding out what you really think about losing weight - here are some examples that I have frequently heard:

"I can't walk past the fridge without opening it."
"I just feel hungry all the time."

"I feel deprived when I'm dieting."

"Diets are boring."

You can tap for any of the above and more with EFT and expect to see real benefits.

The following is taken from a conversation I had recently with a client about the benefits of long-term tapping with EFT. During the conversation we touched on the subject of using EFT for weight loss. Although I have not added a name here this quote is used with full consent of the client.

"I have never, ever been able to diet in my entire life. It would be a day here or there, even on the first day I would always cheat with something. It was always a completely miserable experience. With EFT it's not so hard. Not only is it not so hard but I understand myself and why I do things so much better. I will sometimes tap for "even though I feel hungry all the time" and then I will either eat something because I really was hungry and it won't be such a big deal and I don't gain weight, or I won't feel hungry anymore. When you are somebody who's overeaten all your life, it's your comfort and your joy, eating can be everything to you and when you have to stop or reduce it it's like there's nothing to turn to. Your comfort is gone it's like a complete abyss, it's so traumatic.

It's such a big deal for so many people, a drug addict can conquer their addiction and be a hero, a food addict can loose a couple of stone and people will say "oh that's nice, why didn't do it five years ago?"

You feel so stupid that you want to eat that thing so much and it makes you want to cry because you can't have it. Why? But if you tap with EFT and say "yes I do really want it and it's alright, I love myself even though I do". Somehow or another, I don't really know how it works, but I love the fact that you can say that and tap and it's not a big deal anymore. And I've been able to stick at this for a long time, for me, it's been two months now, and I've lost weight. I'm going to continue and I'll lose all of it – and I'll lose it with EFT. I'm not going to weight watchers or on any fixed program, I just look at what I eat and decide if it's got too much fat in it for me. I have even been known to tap my desires away in the supermarket!"

This quote is intended as an illustration of the possibilities of using EFT with a program of your choice. Many times I am asked "what do I say" or "how can I do this" that is why this book contains many examples and extracts from real life experience in the hope that you will see for yourself the flexibility of EFT and gain some insight into ways you can use it for yourself.

Sound Sleep

I have been personally using and recommending to clients for years acupressure self-help routines to promote a good nights rest and have always found it very effective. As EFT is based on the same principle I had expected that it would also be useful for dealing with sleep difficulties - and it is.

The most effective way of using EFT for sleep problems is to focus your attention on what is stopping you from sleeping.

Are you worried about something you have to face in the future?

Are you generally anxious?

Is your head just too busy with thoughts or plans?

Or still occupied with what you've been doing during the day?

Do you have any physical discomforts or tensions?

Whatever you feel the cause to be tap a few rounds for it in the way you have already learned.

If you have a long standing sleep problem try and think back to when it began and isolate your core emotions about the problem (e.g. anger, overwhelm, fear etc.) once you have resolved these feelings using EFT you will be well on the way to restoring a healthy sleep pattern.

If you are not sure where to begin with this process or don't have any ready ideas about the possible root cause you could try the "investigating root causes" approach on page 67

Working with Children

EFT is, in my experience, a profoundly effective technique for working with children.

From toddler upsets and tantrums through to exam pressures and confidence issues EFT excels across the board.

I think that EFT should be available to all parents - not only does it resolve upsets in children but it facilitates a greater empathy and understanding of their plight from us as parents. This is a win-win situation. If we have a greater understanding of our children's troubles combined with a convenient and effective tool that actually makes them feel better on a deep and genuine level then we will be facilitating a confident and capable adulthood.

I use EFT frequently with my daughter who is two and a half years old. At first she would protest so I would use proxy tapping (see note) on myself for her benefit but eventually she got used to the idea and got wise to the fact that EFT actually made her feel better if she was upset or angry. Even I, a committed EFT enthusiast, have been surprised on many occasions by the rapid transformation from tears to laughter that EFT produces in small children.

To give you some ideas if you would like to use EFT in this way here are some of the more popular areas where we have used EFT with children:

School worries: shyness, lack of confidence, exam nerves, and performance pressure

Calming down and soothing pain after a fall

Nightmares and bad dreams

Poor sleep habits

Anxieties…

Note - if you would like to know more about proxy or surrogate tapping please read Silvia Hartmann-Kent's Adventures in EFT.

CHAPTER 9

Supplementary Techniques

EFT Variations

EFT is not a technique set in stone. In this section we will look at some extra points and variations you may like to try when working with these techniques.

The first procedure I will mention here is called the "9 Gamut" it is a fine tuning exercise which can be used in between EFT sequences like a sandwich:

Tapping Sequence (Bread)

9 Gamut (Cheese)

Tapping Sequence (Bread)

THE 9 GAMUT PROCEDURE

The purpose of the 9 gamut is to "fine tune" the brain and it does this by using some eye movements/positions, humming and counting. It is understood, that via connecting nerves, certain areas of the brain are contacted and stimulated when the eyes are moved. This fact will be familiar to anyone who has studied NLP or Kinesiology. Likewise, different hemispheres of the brain are engaged when you hum a tune or count. The right (or creative) side of the brain is engaged in humming and the left (the logical or linear side) is engaged when counting. Again, anyone familiar with Kinesiology, in particular Three in One, Edu-k and Brain Gym, will know that much importance is placed upon the hemispheres of the brain working in harmony with each other.

The 9 Gamut procedure is a ten second process which incorporates 9 "brain stimulating" actions while continuously tapping on a key point on the triple warmer meridian, which for the purposes of EFT is known as the gamut point (see diagram). Experience has shown that this routine often enhances the EFT process.

To use this procedure tap the gamut point continuously while performing the 9 steps outlined below:

1. **Close your eyes**
2. **Then open them again**
3. **Look hard down right (while holding the head steady).**
4. **Look hard down left (while holding the head steady).**
5. **Roll your eyes in a full circle in one direction.**
6. **Now roll them in a full circle in the opposite direction.**
7. **Hum a couple of seconds of a familiar tune.**
8. **Count rapidly from one two five.**
9. **Hum a couple of seconds of a tune again.**

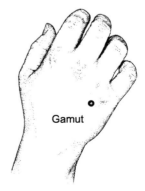

Gamut

That's the 9 gamut. Once you have tried it a couple of times you will see that it is easy to remember and use. The order of steps 1-6 is not so important so don't worry if you jumble the order up. Steps 7-9 should be performed in sequence though as they facilitate rapid switching between the right and left hemisphere of the brain.

Touch and Breathe (TAB)

This is a variation on the original EFT procedure which was developed by John Diepold. Touch and Breathe uses exactly the same points as the EFT sequence but instead of tapping the points it contacts them with a light touch (with 2 - 4 fingers depending on the location of the point) while a full respiration is taken.

The procedure is the same as EFT in all other respects. Some clients at our centre prefer this and refer to it as "socially acceptable EFT". Not everyone feels comfortable about being seen tapping in public but most are very happy with the alternative of holding the points lightly one after the other while taking a natural breathe in and out. This provides an inconspicuous approach that can be used in any situation.

I have had clients tell me that they use this approach in meetings or on the train if they feel the need to tap but would rather not draw attention to themselves.

Some Extra EFT Points

The following are additional potent points which you may add to the EFT routine or substitute for other points if you wish.

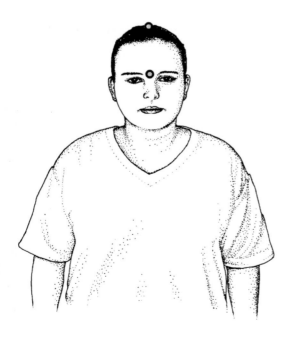

Crown

This point is situated on the Governing Meridian (Ref. GV20). In traditional Chinese medicine it is referred to as the "hundred meeting point" due to it being an important convergence point.

The Third Eye Point

This is a special point, also found on the Governing Meridian (Ref. GV24.5). This point is very soothing to the mind when contacted lightly. In Ayurvedic medicine one key treatment involves dripping warm oil on to this point for balancing and calming the entire system.

The Thymus Tap

Tapping over, or around, the sternum (or breastbone) stimulates the thymus gland. This is a very beneficial exercise that is well worth using regularly as a general maintenance procedure.

To stimulate this area first cup your hand as if you were going to drink water from it, then place it palm side down over the breastbone area (see diagram) and tap firmly but lightly over and around this whole area for about 20 seconds. If you keep your hand loose and flat then the heel of your hand will contact the area at the same time as your fingers.

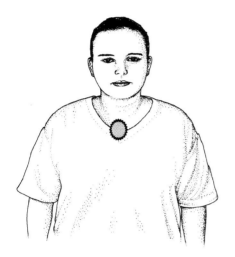

The Thymus Tap benefits:

- Boosts the immune system

- Reduces stress

- Stimulates energy system

- Increases vitality

Tapping the thymus area is grounding. It is a good way of calling your energies together and boosting the flow of vital energy throughout the system.

You can also briskly tap the EFT collarbone point with all your fingers bunched together before tapping the thymus area for an extra boost. The EFT collarbone points is K27 the final point of the Kidney Meridian and it is the neurological centre of the energy system. Tapping this point boosts the circulation of chi energy and encourages it to flow in the correct direction throughout the meridian system.

Stimulating the K27 (or Collarbone points):

- Increases energy
- Relieves constant tiredness
- Enhances the function of the immune system
- Boosts and corrects the flow of vital energy

To re-align your body's energies using these points you can tap the point situated on the left side of your body with the right hand and vice versa with your free hand placed over your navel area.

An alternative to tapping the points you can use the above hand positions to stimulate the points with a firm circular pressure. You can continue this for 20-30 seconds or until any tenderness in the points is relieved.

This is a good technique to use routinely at the start of each day. Clearing these points on a regular basis facilitates clearer thinking, improved vision and perception.

Long Term Tapping with EFT

EFT is too new for us to truly assess the benefits of long term tapping in terms of several years. But we can say that what we have seen so far from those who have been using it regularly for months is very encouraging.

EFT provides rapid relief from a vast array of emotional and physical states it also supports maintenance and balance of health. To use EFT only as a "break glass in case of emergency" technique is almost a disservice.

Regular tapping with EFT has accumulative benefits which should not be missed. Many who have been using it over a period of time report consistently improved clarity of thought, a better sense of their personal resources and a generally calmer and more positive outlook.

EFT is, in my opinion, the ultimate personal development tool. It can be used in so many ways to remove blockages and develop abilities from the little things that make life a bit easier going, to monumental achievements.

Final Word

I hope that you have found this workbook of value and that the examples and descriptions presented have given you some idea of the benefits available to you from using these powerful techniques.

In conclusion, I would like to express my gratitude and appreciation to Gary Craig, the developer of EFT, for his extremely generous and pioneering spirit in making these techniques available to all. And to Silvia Hartmann-Kent, Chris Hardisty and the other Directors of the UK Association for Meridian Therapies for their tireless dedication in presenting meridian therapies in a thorough and professional manner. Should you wish to find out more about EFT and the workshops and trainings available please see the resources section at the back of this book.

Additional Information

From Ancient Science to the Power Therapies of the Future...

I have been fascinated by the meridian system for many years. Over the last year in particular I have spent a great deal of time researching the origins of the understanding that has lead to the breakthroughs we are seeing today with meridian based psychotherapies.

In the background and history section of this book I presented general information on the origins of meridian therapies. Here I would like to offer some additional information, for those who may be interested, on the ancient system of Ayurvedic acupuncture the remaining texts of which date back thousands of years and provide great detail of the science behind acupuncture as it is practised today. The Ayurvedic system also offers deep insight into the mind and specific points which exert a positive and balancing influence upon it. This is of particular interest to those of us working with the EFT meridian points.

The medical systems of India and China (Ayurveda and Traditional Chinese Medicine) can be traced back thousands of years through ancient texts giving detailed information on the subtle energy systems of the body. Various techniques are documented for restoring and balancing these energy systems for the benefit of body and mind.

Since President Nixon's visit to China, Acupuncture and the Chinese medical system has become increasingly popular in the west. It's impact has been significant - the World Health Organisation endorses Acupuncture as a true form of therapy which can cure or treat more than 300 types of disease (W.H.O. Chronicle No.34, 1980).

Scholars such as Drs Frank Ross and David Frawley have travelled extensively and researched in great detail the ancient texts of Ayurvedic medicine to provide us with information on the origins of meridian therapies - in particular the science of acupuncture. Dr Ross has established the connection between Ayurveda and Traditional Chinese Medicine and has gone to great lengths to correlate the two systems. He writes:

"Ayurvedic Acupuncture is traditionally termed *BhedanKarma* (meaning "Piercing-Through Therapy), and is part of the traditional Indian method of using pressure points or *marmas*. These methods are generically referred to as *Marma Chikitsa* (Treatment of Marmas). There is an undeniable connection between Marma Chikitsa and what is today recognised as acupuncture."

Dr Kulkarni the Research Guide of Poona University states:

"The Vedic therapeutic methods in India date back to the prehistoric era. Many Chinese travellers had come to India and have written extensively about the local treatment practises." He goes on to cite evidence that people would go to learn the science of acupuncture from Indian experts at Takshashila University (circa 100 B.C.).

Regrettably, the Takshashila University has since been destroyed along with many of the original ancient texts held there during the invasions India has endured over the centuries.

Of the texts that remain the works of the Ayurvedic surgeon, Sushruta dating back some 3,000 years provide detailed accounts of the marmas or pressure points as they are known today. Sushruta states that each marma is a potent centre of prana, or life energy (referred to as Chi in the Chinese medical system). The information presented in these texts also shows the marma points and meridian channels to correlate very closely to the acupuncture points of the Chinese system still in practise today.

Knowledge of the marma points can be used to "kill or cure" depending on the points used and the way they are contacted. This knowledge is still handed down in secret from one generation to the next. The ancient Kelari system of martial arts which travelled from India to Tibet and China with Buddhist monks presents a system of 107 lethal marmas.

The Charaka Samhita refers to a system of *nadis,* or channels which "penetrate the body from the soles of the feet to the crown of the head" and contain prana - the breath of life. Illustrations of the nadi system show it to be identical to the meridian system upon which present day meridian therapies are based.

The Ayurvedic system also presents it's own version of the five elements theory (*pancha mahabhutas)* and a detailed presentation of the law of opposites which has been adopted into the Chinese medical system as the well known theory of yin and yang.

One area of Ayurvedic knowledge which does not seem to have been absorbed into the Traditional Chinese system (although it is present in the Tibetan branch of meridian practices) is the understanding of the three humours - or *tri dosha - vata, pitta and kapha.*

The primary focus of all Ayurvedic intervention is the maintenance or restoration of balance of these three humours. The nadi system of the twelve major meridians is subdivided according to the tri doshas this is indicated in the following table:

HUMOR	ELEMENT	ORGAN/MERIDIAN
VATA	WIND	Large Intestine/Lung
	WATER	Kidney/Bladder
PITTA	ETHER	Liver/Gall Bladder
	FIRE	Heart/Small Intestine
KAPHA	EARTH	Stomach/Spleen
		Pericardium/Triple Warmer

In Ayurvedic acupuncture the triple warmer is referred to as the Tridosha meridian (tri meaning three and dosha meaning humour). The Chinese understanding of the triple warmer is that it controls airs and humours in three different areas of the trunk of the body –the same is true of the Ayurvedic system. In Ayurveda these three areas fall under the domain of the three humours as described above. This gives us some idea of the vital significance of the triple warmer meridian as an access point for the restoration of balance.

Balance of the three humours is essential to our health and spirits; according to the studies of Dr Ross there are four main causes of their aggravation and they are listed here in order of priority:

1.   Mental and emotional factors (stress)
2.   Diet
3.   Lifestyle
4.   Environmental Factors

With this in mind we can see that emotional disruptions are the primary influence of our health on all levels. This further endorses the benefits that meridian therapies such as EFT, which are perfectly tailored to target and dissolve stress and negative emotions, have to offer our health and functionality on all levels.

A further point of interest provided by the Ayurvedic understanding is the significance of key meridian points for the positive influence of the mind and emotions. Over recent years techniques have been explored and developed based upon a discovery that the beginning and end points of the meridian channels are particularly beneficial for relieving stress and emotional upsets. It was this information that formed the basis of Dr Callahan's discovery and formed the basis of his highly effective Thought Field Therapy.

Ayurveda confirms the significance of these points and provides a further understanding of why they are so beneficial in balancing the disruptions of the mind.

Vata is the humour that is related to the mind. According to Ayurveda disturbances of a subtle or emotional nature are always reflected in vata disturbance. The positioning of the meridians and their potent points is set out in a way that provides access to each channel for physical and mental benefit. For grosser, or more physical, manifestations of illness the points on the meridians situated closer to the actual organ concerned are used to restore balnce.

For disturbances of an emotional nature the meridian system contains potent points which are distant from the organs of the torso; such as points on the hands and feet. For the balancing of the vata humour and the mind in general the marma points found at the ends of the fingertips are believed to be especially potent.

As a practitioner of meridian therapies I am fascinated to find that texts dating back thousands of years endorse and confirm what we are repeatedly finding in practice today.

The tables on the following pages provide information on the specific meridian points used in the EFT sequence. This information was primarily researched and compiled by Chris Hardisty and Tom Bolton with a few additions made by myself.

MERIDIANS:	WHEN BLOCKED:	WHEN TAPPED:
EFT Ref. EB (Eyebrow point) Acupuncture Ref. Bl2 BLADDER MERIDIAN Inner Direction Element: WATER Location: At the beginning of the eyebrow just above and to either side of the nose.	Increases fear & inhibition Causes lethargy, restlessness, impatience & forgetfulness. Indicated in phobias	Relieves Trauma. Releases fear and increases courage. Increases energy levels. Unblocks thinking process. Allows free expression & short term memory recall.
EFT Ref. SE (Side of Eye) Acupuncture Ref. GB1 GALL BLADDER MERIDIAN Harmony Element: WOOD Location: On the bone bordering the outside corner of the eye.	Depletes energy. Causes cloudy judgement, impairs ability to make decisions. Is related to open rage or wrath. Inhibits recovery from shock. Causes anxiety patterns.	Relieves lethargy and increases energy levels. Reinforces determination. Enables decision making & gives clarity of thought. Is calming.
EFT Ref. UE (Under Eye) Acupuncture Ref. St2 STOMACH MERIDIAN Contentment Element: EARTH Location: On the bone under the eye approx. an inch below and in line with the pupil.	Causes confused thought patterns, disorientation and worry. Obsessive thinking, compulsions and addictions are connected to this meridian.	Clears thought patterns and is grounding. Integrates intellectual and intuitive processes. Creates sense of harmony with home and family, nourishment and contentment. Useful in the treatment of addictive urges, anxiety and feelings of deprivation.
EFT Ref. UN (Under Nose) Acupuncture Ref. GV26 GOVERNING VESSEL Inner Connection Acupuncture Potent Point: "Middle of a Person" Location: Centre of upper lip	Causes introvert behaviour. Embarrassment, & panic.	Removes shyness and increases ability to communicate with others. Removes feelings of panic and relieves shock. Relieves embarrassment. Hunger control centre. Important in treatment of allergies.

MERIDIANS:	WHEN BLOCKED:	WHEN TAPPED:
EFT Ref. Ch (Chin point) Acupuncture Ref. CV24 CENTRAL VESSEL Self Empowerment Location: In the centre of the chin, midway between point of chin and bottom lip.	Holds past traumatic emotions.	Promotes free circulation of chi energy. Removes fatigue & strengthens system. Alleviates feelings of shame. Dissolves feelings of panic & anxiety
EFT Ref. CB (Collarbone) Acupuncture Ref. K27 KIDNEY MERIDIAN Gentle Spirit Acupressure Potent Point: Elegant Mansion Element: WATER Location: The junction where breastbone and collarbone meet	Low Energy. Fear. Indecision & hesitancy. Little willpower. Poor confidence.	Provides willpower & impetus to carry out tasks. Promotes gentleness. Relieves mental strain. Pain control centre. Important point for entire body mind system. Ensures correct meridian flow throughout entire network.
EFT Ref. UA (Under Arm) Acupuncture Ref. Sp.21 SPLEEN MERIDIAN Choice Making Element: EARTH Location: On the side of the body approx. 4 inches below armpit.	Slows down thought process. Poor concentration & indecision. Feeling drained or "burnt out". Overly concerned with opinions of others. Addictive tendencies.	Clears thought process, improves concentration & provides ability for good decision making. Relieves anxiety & addictive urges. Ability to take life as it comes. Assimilation both mentally & physically - digestion.
EFT Ref. Th (Thumbnail) Acupuncture Ref. Lu11 LUNG MERIDIAN Worth Element: Metal Location: Outside edge of the thumb at the base of the nail.	Negative emotions of sadness & depression. Grief. Produces resentment. Causes lethargy and low energy. Inflexible nature.	Releases negativity & increases vitality. Provides free will & individuality. Relevant in treatment of OCD. Dissolves disdain & increases tolerance. Increases intuition and promotes a positive outlook.

MERIDIANS:	WHEN BLOCKED:	WHEN TAPPED:
EFT Ref. IF (Index Finger) Acupuncture Ref. LI1 LARGE INTESTINE MERIDIAN Letting Go Element: METAL Location: At side of the base of the finger nail (same point as on thumb).	Causes nostalgia. Holding on to past hurts, inability to forgive. Stubbornness. Mental "constipation". Resentment. Guilt.	Relieves guilt. Frees emotions that hold a person to living in the past. Provides understanding of positive present tense. Optimism & future planning. Dissolves resentment & provides capacity for understanding and forgiving.
EFT Ref. MF (Middle Finger) Acupuncture Ref. PC9 PERICARDIUM MERIDIAN (HEART PROTECTOR) Bonding Element: FIRE Location: At side of the base of the finger nail (same point as on thumb).	Causes low-self esteem. Expressions of cruelty & hard-hearted behaviour. Jealousy. Restlessness. Short-term depression. Self-absorption, coldness, lack of concern for others. Lack of enthusiasm.	Releases feelings of inferiority. Dissolves jealousy. Relives regret. Clears allergies (airborne type). Promotes a sense of humour. Impetus for advancing conscious-ness.
EFT Ref. LF (Little Finger) Acupuncture Ref. H9 HEART MERIDIAN Unconditional Love Element: FIRE Location: At side of the base of the finger nail (same point as on thumb).	Chest pains: anger, selfishness & loneliness. Deep sorrow & depres-sion. Hastiness. Arrogance. Yearning for love. Responsible for extreme emo-tional responses. Hysteria & er-ratic behaviour.	Encourages development of empa-thy, compassion and uncondi-tional love. Removes limited thinking & opens up consciousness. Improves long term memory. Promotes joy, optimism, tranquil-lity, emotional & spiritual growth. Emotional balance & control of thoughts and senses.
EFT Ref. KC (Karate Chop) Acupuncture Ref. SI3 SAMLL INTESTINE MERIDIAN Trust Element: FIRE Location: The middle of the fleshy part on the outside of the hand.	Lack of confidence and feelings of self-hatred. Causes cloudy judgement & hesi-tancy. Responsible for anxiety patterns & slow recovery from shock. Forgetfulness.	Relevant in treatment of psycho-logical reversal. Removes self– hatred and doubt. Increases self-esteem & confi-dence. Assists memory. Improves ability to recover from shock.

MERIDIANS:	WHEN BLOCKED:	WHEN TAPPED:
EFT Ref. GS (Gamut Spot) Acupuncture Ref. TW3 TRIPLE WARMER MERIDIAN Connection Element: FIRE Location: On the back of the hand, approx. half an inch behind the middle of the knuckles of the ring and little fingers.	Inability to express love and emotions. Tendency to over strive. Exhaustion. Causes emotional coldness. Desire for isolation. Dizziness. Responsible for unsociable nature/behaviour.	Provides impetus for warm emotional interaction with others. Social & communication skills. Release point for emotional garbage, resentment and past problems. Physical pain relief point. Useful in relief of despair, depression & loneliness.

Researched & Compiled by Chris Hardisty, Tom Bolton & Ananga Sivyer

FREQUENTLY ASKED QUESTIONS ABOUT EFT

Q: Are the points only on one side of the body?

A: No - (with the exception of the under nose and chin points which are central) all EFT points are symmetrically located on either side of the body. You can tap on either side of the body and with either hand.

Q: Are there any side effects?

A: Serious side effects resulting from the application of EFT are extremely rare. From statistical research, Gary Craig states that *"out of an estimated 10 000 applications of these energy tapping procedures, only 20 such cases were reported. This approximates 0.2%"*.

Q: Does EFT help everyone?

A: The success rate of EFT is estimated at between 50-99% according to the skill and experience of the therapist or individual using it. It has been found after statistical research that there is a small percentage (1-5%) of people that receive little benefit from the application of EFT. However, EFT is only 5 years old and is being continuously developed and reviewed so it is possible that even that small percentage may be reduced yet further over time.

Q: Why is the ring finger excluded when tapping?

A: The meridian running down the ring finger is the triple warmer meridian and is already covered at other stages of the EFT procedure. Specifically when tapping the gamut point, it is also often tapped at the same time as the side of the eye point as the triple warmer meridian ends close to this point.

Some reactions that may occur as a result of using EFT are:

Tiredness

Sometimes after an EFT session a person will feel tired and sleepy. This often follows a treatment where there has been frequent yawning. That yawning is usually indicative of an energy shift or release and resting is your body's way of adjusting to this positive change.

I have on a few occasions noticed that when several rounds of tapping were used in succession for deep-rooted emotions that yawning often occurs at one or two particular meridian points in each round.

An example of this is one lady who recently yawned every time we tapped the index finger point for four consecutive rounds of tapping. On the fifth round, as an experiment, I tapped the index finger point just two or three times before quickly moving on to the next finger but it still produced a yawn! When I considered the nature of the problem we were working with it was obvious that the nature of it was likely to be reflected in the lung meridian, which is contacted at the index finger point. That point is related to "letting go" and forgiveness and yawning repeatedly at that meridian point is a positive indication that that is exactly what was happening.

"Mellow" Feeling

I have used the word "mellow" because that is the word used by most of the people I have worked with who have experienced it. It is often the case when we are presenting workshops that one or two people will become very relaxed and quite dreamy. These are, more often than not, people who have released a large amount of tension during the tapping sequences.

All tapping is good for you!

Tapping reduces stress and benefits the immune system greatly – regular long-term tapping is extremely beneficial in facilitating clarity and focus and bringing us in touch with our natural resources and abilities. Tapping is good for you on every level and it is extremely unlikely that you will experience any adverse reactions from it.

Resources

&

Contact Information

The Association for Meridian Energy Therapies

The Association For Meridian Therapies was formed in 1998 and is the oldest existing professional body for the new Meridian Energy Therapies.

It is our aim to bring Meridian Therapies to the attention of the public and fellow professionals world-wide.

To this end, we have created a referring organisation of Meridian Therapists to co-ordinate our efforts to publicise and educate all members of society to the benefits to mind, body and spirit that Meridian Therapies bring.

For further information, articles and access to our on-line communities please visit us at:

www.TheAMT.com

ABOUT THE AUTHOR:

Ananga Sivyer is a bold pioneer and leader in the rapidly expanding field of Meridian Therapies. Since establishing her company, Chandra PDS, in 1999 she has been actively promoting the Emotional Freedom Techniques (EFT) via health shows and popular workshops nation-wide. Ananga is a Licensed Trainer for the Association for Meridian Therapies and is widely known for her lively and enthusiastic style of presentation.

Her career in complimentary medicine began in 1989 when she trained with Anne Gillanders at the British School of Reflexology. Since then she has expanded her skills to include acupressure, kinesiology, Meridian Psychotherapies, NLP, Time Line Therapy and Humanistic Neuro-Linguistic Psychology.

Ananga is currently practising as a therapist in Kent and London and is actively involved in training other therapists to incorporate Meridian Therapies into their existing skills. She loves teaching and has a strong desire to see these incredibly liberating techniques become a household name.

If you would like full details of the workshops offered by Chandra PDS you can contact Ananga at:

Chandra PDS
Richardsons Farm, Crowhurst Lane,
West Kingsdown, Kent TN15 6JE U K

Telephone: +44 (0)1474 853576

Email: info@chandra-pds.co.uk
Website: www.chandra-pds.co.uk